# C. C. ROUSE

D1097359

# Montana Bullwhacker

**Pacific Press®**
Publishing Association

Nampa, Idaho | Oshawa, Ontario, Canada
www.pacificpress.com

Cover design by Steve Lanto
Cover design resources from iStockphoto.com
Inside design by Kristin Hansen-Mellish
Originally published in 1969.

The author assumes full responsibility for the accuracy of all facts and
quotations as cited in this book.

Scriptures quotations marked KJV are from the King James Version.

You can obtain additional copies of this book by calling toll-free
1-800-765-6955 or by visiting www.adventistbookcenter.com.

ISBN 13: 978-0-8163-5545-7
ISBN 10: 0-8163-5545-2

February 2015

# TABLE OF CONTENTS

# 1
# THE TRAIL DIVIDES

The Nebraska prairie land lay warm and green under the setting sun of a June evening in the year 1861. For a mile a train of covered wagons, their white canopies covered with dust from their long journey, straggled in a wide procession through the prairie grass.

Elisha Rouse, fifteen, small for his age and tough as a rawhide whip, trotted beside a team of ponies hitched to a small wagon in the center of the train. His older brother Elliot, on the high wagon seat, held in his horses with a tight rein. They had caught the smell of water, along with all the other animals in the train, and only quick, firm action prevented them from bolting for the river.

Lisha shaded his eyes against the lowering sun and tried to see the river and the houses. Like the horses, he felt an urge to rush forward. Then he saw the settlement loom up in the prairie sunset, and his alert brown eyes took in every detail of the sprawling buildings. "So this is North Platte!" he exclaimed.

His brother did not acknowledge his announcement. After all, what could the cluster of buildings they looked upon be if not North Platte? Still, Lisha reflected, they had looked forward to North Platte for a long time—almost a month.

Now Elliot took his pipe from his mouth, his face never relaxing its severe expression. "Lisha, this is the last real settlement." He raised his voice above the noise of the caravan. "We must decide."

For a week they'd talked about it—longer than that—ever since they'd left Franklin County, Minnesota, to follow the trail west. When they reached North Platte, the real West would begin.

They'd been so hopeful back in Minnesota. The West with its promise of a free, adventuresome life had seemed the brightest prospect within their vision. Now neither of them felt so sure about the gold and the valuable furs. Along the trail they'd traveled, they'd heard discouraging reports. They'd seen disappointed men returning from the fabulous land of gold.

5

Many of them had lost everything. Sick and disillusioned, they turned back to the settled East with its known security, farms, gardens, and pastures full of contented herds grazing the rich grass.

Lisha knew that these encounters and the news the men brought had discouraged Elliot, not from going west, but from going to California. Now, here in North Platte, they must make a final decision. Should they go on with the wagon train to California, or should they strike out on their own?

Lisha knew, of course, that the decision must be Elliot's. Twenty-five years old, married, with two young sons, Elliot had much more at stake than Lisha, ten years younger. Yes, Elliot must decide.

"We have to make up our minds now, Lisha." Elliot's voice rose behind him. "Shall we go on to California, or shall we head toward Oregon?" He flicked the reins over the ponies' backs. "We have to decide while we're here at North Platte."

"Yes, I know." Lisha wanted to say more. He knew what he wanted—a chance to own some of this rich land, to carve out a place for himself in the fertile wilderness, to settle in the free open West where a man could reach high, spread far, put down roots into virgin soil. Although he preferred to go toward Oregon, he knew from past experience that he must not seem too eager, must pretend indifference.

"Speak up, fella," Elliot urged. "You're most a man already."

Lisha still said nothing.

"For my part," Elliot went on, "I'm for striking out for Oregon. I figure those California goldfields are about petered out."

"Oregon's fine with me," Lisha said. "The land's so big and rich, doesn't make much difference, I reckon."

The crawling wagons reached the river at last, and while the evening darkness fell around them, the travelers made camp. Eager animals quenched their thirst, and noisy children waded in the shallow water. All around them, Lisha could hear the comfortable sounds of wood being split for the evening fire and kettles clinking together. Later, the mingled fragrance of many suppers being cooked in the open intensified his already ravenous hunger.

Lisha knew that the train would probably spend the next day or two here on the Platte River, where the women would do their washing and the animals could graze.

Next morning, Lisha wakened to all the noises of the wagon train at rest. Cocks crowed, dogs barked, cattle lowed, and always the children mingled their shouts with every other noise. He smelled coffee, bacon, and campfire smoke. For a few seconds, he puzzled over where he could be. Then awareness came with a rush. They were camped at North Platte, and Elliot had already rolled out and had built a fire.

Lisha pulled on his clothes and picked up the coffeepot and a bag of hominy grits. Sleepy-eyed, he looked for the mush kettle, and then he saw that Elliot had already put the kettle over the fire.

"Today's the day," Elliot said, dishing himself a bowl of mush. "You still feel like going to Oregon?"

"Yes, if you do."

The brothers ate in silence. Lisha wondered what Melissa and the two little boys were doing this June morning.

"Good thing we didn't bring Melissa and the kids," Elliot said as though he read his brother's mind. "The trail will be hard and dangerous for tough fellows like us—no place for women and kids." Elliot lighted his pipe and looked off into the distance with that fierce, intense gaze.

"Well, we've got a few of the right things to start life in the West." He turned his searching look on his younger brother. "We've got strong, tough muscles, and we've got a hankering for the rough, free life. We're used to hard work, and that's got to stand us in place of money."

Lisha looked up and saw a stranger walking toward them. "Who's that, Elliot? Looks like a farmer."

Elliot went to meet the man. He looked even more like a farmer at close range, but he smiled and shook hands with the brothers. "We've got a big hay harvest, and we're short of hands." He looked from one brother to the other, and Lisha noticed that his scrutiny rested a little longer on him. Did the farmer question whether he, a fifteen-year-old, could hold up his end of a haying job?

The farmer seemed to have come to a decision. "Would you fellows like a job in the hay for a few weeks?"

"We've decided to leave the wagon train here." Elliot looked the farmer over, and Lisha could see that he approved of the man. "A few days in the hayfield sounds good to me. What about you, Lish?"

They discussed wages and other arrangements. The Rouse brothers would pull their covered wagon to the farm and sleep in it. They would eat at the farmer's table. They arrived at the farm in time for a big dinner.

When they went out to join the farm hands for the afternoon of work in the hay meadows, they passed the kitchen window and Lisha overheard one of the women busy with the dishes say, "My goodness, did you see that little new fellow eat?"

Lisha knew they must be talking about him. After all, he hadn't eaten a good woman-cooked meal for a month, and he felt hungry all the time. At fifteen, he supposed that such an appetite must be normal for a boy. He hoped so. He could still taste the hot biscuits with fresh-churned butter and honey, good fresh eggs, all the milk he could drink, roast beef and potatoes, new garden peas, lettuce—yes, he'd eaten all he could hold. His stomach felt tight, but good—real good!

After supper, they lingered to listen to the talk of the men gathered on the farmhouse porch. They talked of gold and the rich land in the West, but mostly they talked of the dangers. "I just heard today," one of them said, "of a couple of wagons that tried to slip from Laramie up through the Indian territory to the goldfields. Indians caught them and killed them all."

"Yes," another man agreed, "the only way to get through is to go in such large wagon trains that the Indians can be fought off. The trails into the Idaho country are littered with bones of foolish adventurers."

That night, when he and Elliot had settled down in their wagon, Elliot said, "You know, Lish, I figure we've done the right thing. The more I think about it, the more I'm sure there's big opportunity in the Northwest. There's other things besides gold—there's land."

"Danger too!" Lisha remembered the men's talk after supper and felt a pleasant thrill run up his spine. "There's Indians—lots of them, and fierce too. The men who've come out here to make a living are rough and tough."

"Yes, from what we've seen, they're surely that." Elliot lighted his pipe and leaned back against the tailgate. "I don't mind. I can be as rough and tough as the best of them and as quick on the draw. We'll probably find hunting and fishing better than anything either of us ever knew back in Minnesota. Should be easy to make a good living."

Lisha lay awake after Elliot settled down to sleep, and he thought about his brother. Elliot looked so severe and seemed so eager to pick fights with anyone who challenged him, yet Lisha knew that at heart no one could be more generous or more persuasive. He could talk almost anyone into almost anything. And Lisha never doubted his brother's deep affection.

He looked over and saw, in the sharp moonlight, the shape of a book Elliot had been reading for weeks. He couldn't read the name, but he knew it: *The Age of Reason,* by Thomas Paine. Sometimes Elliot read aloud, and Lisha had decided that he didn't like that book. It seemed to make a mockery of God. He'd always had respect for God.

Lisha wished that Elliot didn't drink and smoke, yet in spite of his faults, Elliot gave him a feeling of security. Together they would make a good team. They'd find a place and clear a farm in some valley with deep, rich soil. Then Elliot could send for Melissa and the little boys.

The second day at the farm the farmer came by and praised their work. "You're doing all right, even the little feller. Pure coiled steel spring, he is." The man laughed. "I'd like you to stay on through haying; longer if you will."

Elliot leaned on his fork and scratched his head. "We'll stay through haying. Then I think we'd better push on. We want to get settled somewhere before winter sets in."

The farmer hesitated. "I hate to see two good fellas like you get out in that wild Indian country. Them Indians are getting madder by the day. They do resent the white settlers coming in and digging for gold and shooting the buffalo."

The summer passed, and almost every day the Rouse brothers heard of Indian attacks on wagon trains or of new gold strikes or some other thrilling news of the great wild western country. The brothers turned brown, and their muscles tightened under the steady work. Lisha even grew a little taller. He never seemed able to hold all he wanted to eat.

At evening time, alone in their own covered wagon, Lisha and Elliot nourished their dream of the West and its promise. The nearer they approached to its adventure, the more determined they became to press on westward.

In early autumn, they bade the farmer and his family goodbye, hitched the ponies to their wagon, and headed west on the trail to Laramie.

# 2
# INDIANS!

Jolting along in the old covered wagon on the trail to Laramie, the Rouse brothers did not talk much. Elliot had to handle the horses with alert firmness. Lisha sat beside him on the high wagon seat or sometimes got down to run alongside to keep his legs exercised.

They drove through lonely country. Small bands of Indians lurked in the draws. Buffalo grazed the prairie grass. A wide and lonely country, this western America. Lisha thrilled to a sense of impending adventure, of big and important things about to happen, of danger and desperate encounters with who knew what?

"Do you remember we heard in North Platte that drivers are needed for the central division of the Great Overland Stages?" Lisha turned to Elliot. "That'd be real living!"

Elliot spoke without removing his pipe from his mouth. "Seems to me I did hear something about a shortage of drivers. Must be the war." He frowned at Lisha. "Hear they use real young fellas sometimes. Most dangerous thing a man can do lawfully, I reckon."

"Yes, I know." Lisha settled down to his own thoughts again. Maybe, since he'd just passed his sixteenth birthday, they'd give him a job. After all, what did a man's life amount to if he couldn't face danger and adventure?

They found Fort Laramie buzzing with rumors and feverish excitement. News of fresh gold strikes at Elk City, Orofino, and Florence in the Idaho country had filled the place with unrest.

Although much of Wyoming and the vast Northwest had been reserved under treaty for the Indians, the white men pressing into the alluring West had little regard for the Indians' hunting grounds and often acted as though no treaty existed. Many emigrants who had started for California abandoned their original plans just as Lisha and Elliot had done. They crowded Laramie now with eager plans and determined action. Neither the slowness of travel nor the danger and difficulty of the trail discouraged the gold-hungry men in their first frenzy over a new gold strike in the mysterious West.

In Laramie, Lisha and Elliot bought Western clothes—new buckskin jackets and pants and high-crowned, wide-brimmed hats.

The man who sold the clothes asked, "You fellas new here?"

"Yes, we just drove our wagon in yesterday," Elliot said. "We came from North Platte."

The man looked Elliot over with new respect. "You mean you drove all alone—not in a wagon train?"

"We came by ourselves."

The man reached his hand across the counter. "You can't know how lucky you are. Didn't you see any Indians?" Elliot shook his head.

"Well, don't do it again. I mean don't go venturing out by yourselves. Not many live to tell the story of such foolishness." The man wrapped up the old homespun clothes. "It's dangerous for whites to pass through the Indian territory. If they had caught you, they would have burned your wagon and left your bones by the trail."

Elliot took a job at the post while Lisha spent a few days looking around and studying the people, especially those around the stagecoach station.

One day Lisha overheard some men talking about someone named McClellan. From the conversation, he concluded that the man must be a stagecoach driver. Lisha looked him up and entered into conversation with him. He helped him with his horses and with loading his stage.

"How old are you, kid?" McClellan asked him.

Lisha drew himself up to his full height. "Sixteen," he said and hoped he knew the reason why McClellan had asked.

"The big boss needs men badly, kid. Why don't you try to get on as a stage hand, or maybe a driver? You're right handy with horses. You're quick and tough."

"I'd like nothing better." Lisha felt a thrill of excitement stir in his middle.

"Come with me. I'll take you to Slade."

Lisha caught his breath. Slade! Must be Joseph A. Slade, superintendent of the central division. He trembled with eagerness.

The superintendent looked him over with interest. McClellan spoke up. "He's a likely kid, Joe, quick and smart; and I reckon he's not afraid of anything."

"Where are you from, son?"

"Originally from Michigan." Lisha looked the great man straight in the eye. "But I've lived in Franklin County, Minnesota, for the last nine years."

Slade studied the youth for a long time before speaking. Lisha began to be embarrassed under the man's searching gaze. He knew that Slade could estimate his age. He was still a lot shorter than Elliot. He also knew that the Civil War had begun to affect even these remote places. Dependable men were hard to get.

Then the superintendent began to talk to Lisha as a father talks to his son, with earnest kindness. "I can give you a job, son; but I wonder if I should. You might not live to enjoy it very long." He watched Lisha's face. "Our Overland Stages [later bought by Wells Fargo] run through six hundred miles of the most dangerous and lonely trails in America. Few white settlers live there, and wild Indians roam the whole length and breadth of the region."

The more Joseph Slade talked, the more Lisha wanted that job, and he knew that his eagerness must show on his face.

"Some parts of the stage route," Slade went on, "are overrun by wild, reckless men who live by their pistols and bowie knives. We call them road agents, and robbing a stagecoach is everyday adventure for them—their pleasure and their profit."

He paused and continued to study Lisha. "I take it you know how to handle horses."

Lisha caught at the glimmer of hope he detected in the kind voice. "I don't know much of anything else," he replied.

"Well, son, I'll give you a job if you want it. Maybe I'll regret it, but I'm desperate." Again, he looked Lisha over for a long time. "I have a few rules that you must promise to obey. First—no drinking. Stay out of saloons. Second—don't get in fights. Men out here fight with guns and knives, and they fight to kill." He hesitated. "On the other hand, don't let anyone run over you. There'll be times when you must take a stand. At such times, be quick and accurate and try to foresee what the other fellow's next move is going to be."

Joseph Slade looked down at Lisha with kindness in his eyes. "You still want the job?"

"Thanks a lot, Mr. Slade. When do I start?"

Some of Slade's competent men taught Lisha to repair harnesses. They taught him to set the iron rims on the wooden wagon wheels. An experienced blacksmith showed him how to shoe horses. Then Slade sent him to a stage station managed by an old-timer in the West, Uncle Rube.

Lisha discovered that he had not known much about the stagecoach business, but he did know about horses. Here at the lonely stage stop, he learned fast. His heart always quickened at the sight of the stage coming round the curve, its six horses in full gallop while the stage bounced and swayed over the rough trail.

Uncle Rube showed him how to unhitch the tired horses and hitch fresh ones to the stage in the fastest way possible, while the driver and his passengers rested for a few minutes. Then, with a flourish and a shout, they rattled off again in a cloud of dust or a spatter of mud according to the prevailing weather.

Since hay cost a great deal, Lisha grazed the horses on the prairie grass. Before time for the stage to arrive, he brought them in, fed them some grain, and curried and harnessed them. When the stage whirled into the yard, he had the fresh horses all ready to hook up in a hurry.

Late one afternoon just before sunset, Lisha noticed a cloud of dust far down the trail. He called Uncle Rube's attention to it.

The old man studied the dust cloud for a moment. "Indians!" he said.

"How can you know when they are so far away?"

"Son, when you've lived with danger as long as I have, you'll just know!"

Uncle Rube contemplated the approaching menace an instant longer. "Those thieving Indians are after the horses, and they won't mind scalping us and burning the relay station." He ordered Lisha to bring in the horses, harness them, lead them into a thicket, and tie them there.

Now Uncle Rube began loading his weapons. "When they don't find the horses, they'll burn the station."

They gathered up the rifles, pistols, and ammunition and took up a covered position not far from the buildings. Uncle Rube showed Lisha where to stand. "Now when we open up on them, we'll shoot, then jump about four feet and shoot again as quick as we can. Make them think there are a lot of us."

Lisha stood waiting. He saw that Uncle Rube had no compunction about shooting Indians. To him they were a bunch of pesky varmints. He often said that dead Indians were the only good ones he'd ever seen.

Now Lisha heard the pounding hooves of the Indian ponies. Darkness drew down fast. The Indians stormed the corral, and finding no horses there, they turned to the station with wild howls and brandishing of firebrands. Lisha held his breath with excitement. Yes, they had set the place on fire. He remembered that rain had fallen a few days back and hoped the flames wouldn't start a prairie fire. He wondered why Uncle Rube didn't shoot.

Then Uncle Rube gave the signal, and Lisha knew that his hand on the rifle lacked something of being as steady as he wished. Just as he leveled it and aimed, he heard a loud report right in his ear. He jumped to the right about four feet and leveled his gun again. Another report came from Uncle Rube's gun and Lisha jumped again. He had jumped back and forth several times before he realized that he had not yet fired a shot. When he did begin to shoot, the skirmish quickly ended.

The Indians rode away from the burning building and melted into the night. The hoofbeats of their ponies mingled with the night noises of the prairie and vanished in the distance.

Uncle Rube seemed much pleased that they had saved the horses. And when they found a dead Indian, he acted hilarious. "We got one of the varmints!" he exclaimed and went to get his shovel.

Lisha had never looked on a dead man before. Even an Indian stretched out in death impressed him in a way so profound that he couldn't shake it off. The licking flames threw strange lights on the young buck's face, and Lisha hoped that Uncle Rube's bullet, not his, had killed him.

That night as they lay out under the stars with the horses grazing near them, Lisha couldn't help wondering where that young Indian had gone. Somehow horse stealing didn't seem a sin terrible enough to roast a young fellow in hell for thousands of years. The thought bothered him; he couldn't shake it off. He supposed the Bible taught everlasting hellfire; he'd heard many a sermon about it back in Minnesota.

Lisha got a transfer to a swing station—a stop for passengers to get out and stretch while the driver watered his horses and gave them a little time to rest. They always kept a few horses at the swing station in case a horse should become sick or lame and have to be replaced. Lisha must see that fresh drinking water stood ready and waiting when the stagecoach rolled in.

One day he carried fresh water from the spring and filled a barrel as he always did. The stage came flashing in at high speed. The driver drew up with a flourish. He got down from his high seat, grabbed a dipper, and took some water from the barrel. With an oath he spat out the water and pushed the barrel over, dumping the water on the ground. "You stupid kid!" He loosed a string of abusive words on Lisha. "Now fill that barrel with water that's fit to drink."

Lisha put out his hand to take the water bucket when a leathery hand reached over his shoulder and took it from him. He looked up into the angry face of Joseph Slade.

Slade handed the bucket to the surprised driver. "Here, you emptied that barrel. Now fill it!"

Lisha watched Slade, with drawn pistol, supervise the filling of the barrel to the brim. He realized now that only a tough, strong man like Joseph Slade could manage a stagecoach line with success in this wild and lawless country.

Lisha also learned that first winter what Joseph Slade had meant when he said that the road agents forced their way with guns and knives. He saw one duel where the contenders fought with double-barreled shotguns. Viewing the resulting corpse, Lisha thought again of how quickly this young adventurer had been snatched into eternity, and he wondered again about hell and what happens after a man dies.

Late in the winter, Lisha decided that he should go back and see Elliot. Through the deep snow, he rode back to Laramie and found Elliot as glad to see him as though he had been gone for years.

"Well, Lish, you're most growed up." Elliot looked at him with that stern expression he remembered so well. "What do you think of the West now?"

"There's gold to be had in these mountains, Elliot." Lisha had resisted the gold fever through the first part of the winter, but now as he and Elliot recounted all the fabulous stories, they found themselves struck with the same urge that afflicted every man in the West.

"We'll sell the ponies," Elliot said, ready to head out and find his fortune. "Oxen are much better. The Indians don't steal them. They hold up better on the long trails, and we can turn them out to graze and be sure of finding them in the morning."

As soon as the snow began to melt from the trails, the two Rouse brothers struck off alone on the trail from Fort Laramie to the gold fields in Idaho.

# 3
# A NEW GOLD STRIKE

Large wagon trains with adequate protection against Indian attack had made the journey from Laramie to the goldfields in Idaho, but those who attempted to slip through in one or two wagons had almost without exception left their bones beside the trail. Elliot and Lisha knew the danger, yet they made their preparations with a lighthearted disregard of it. Hadn't they driven one lone wagon from North Platte to Laramie?

Lisha had found a little mongrel dog, and it followed him like a shadow.

"I don't know about that dog," Elliot said as they got the covered wagon ready for the trip. "We'll be going through hostile Indian country most of the way, and that dog might bark at the wrong time."

Lisha looked down into the trusting brown eyes of his little dog and said, "He goes with me."

Crow, Sioux, and Cheyenne Indians crossed and recrossed in front and in back of the Rouse brothers' lone wagon as it moved slowly westward through South Pass and then north toward the goldfields in what is now western Montana. But as though under a cloak of invisibility or some protective guidance, they crawled along through the wild, barren country, each evening drawing nearer to their objective.

Jolting along in the covered wagon with only the gentle sounds of nature and the sight of nature's awakening life to stimulate their senses, Lisha and Elliot began to doubt all the fearful stories they had heard about this trail.

Then one morning, when Lisha went out with his dog to look for the oxen, he saw about fifteen horsemen approaching. They must be Indians. He concealed himself in a clump of sagebrush. His little dog seemed to sense the danger and his master's caution. He crouched at Lisha's side without a whimper.

The Indians came straight toward Lisha's hiding place. He knew he hadn't a chance against so many. He had no doubt that within the next few minutes he would be scalped or taken prisoner. His heart pounded so loud that he felt sure the Indians must hear it. The hair bristled on the dog's back; yet he did not bark or utter a sound.

The Indians passed within a few yards of Lisha's hiding place. Lisha crept out, located the oxen, and took them back to the wagon.

"What's the matter, Lish, you sick?" Elliot looked at his brother in concern.

"Elliot, did you see the Indians?" he asked.

"No," Elliot scowled. "I did think I heard the sound of horses' hooves, but I decided it must be my imagination."

"Real Indians!" Lisha caught his breath and sat down by the wagon. "About fifteen of them, and so close I could have hit them with a stone."

"Well, in a few days we'll be among the settlements in the gold country." Elliot hitched the oxen and climbed to the high seat, and Lisha walked along beside the team as they picked their patient way along the trail through the wild, unsettled land. They had gone a good distance before Lisha could quiet his own rapid heartbeat.

Without further incident and with no molestation by anyone, the Rouse brothers came at last to Deer Lodge and staked out mining claims.

Neither of them knew much about gold mining. They had heard stories of "free gold" coming out of the new strikes in Idaho. They understood that "free gold" came from placer mining and that no milling process was necessary to free the gold as in the quartz gold mines in Colorado.

The boys had no success with their first claim, so they moved on to Hell Gate (near the present city of Missoula, Montana), hoping to find something better.

There Lisha saw some of the men preparing fields for planting. He picked out a piece of rich-looking land and sowed it to wheat. Elliot helped, but Lisha could see that Elliot's thoughts and plans lay with the adventuring gold seekers.

Only one shadow marred Lisha's joy in the wild freedom and vast opportunity of the Northwest. Elliot had started drinking again. He had made friends in Hell Gate who influenced him to hang around the saloons and mix in the vulgar talk.

One day as Lisha stood looking over his growing wheat, he thought with a pang of remorse over the months since he had left home. With sudden insight, he realized how far he and Elliot had drifted from their early training. He could scarcely remember his mother. She had died before he had grown old enough to go to school. But his older sister, Helen, had taken Mother's place and carried on the family devotions.

He remembered his mother's Bible. Often, while still a small boy, he had leafed through it, looking at the pictures and reading verses which his mother or his sister Helen had underlined. Now two verses seemed to stand out clearly in his memory as though illuminated: "Woe unto him that buildeth his house by unrighteousness, and his chambers by wrong." "Thine eyes and thine heart are not but for thy covetousness, and for to shed innocent blood, and for oppression, and for violence, to do it." Jeremiah 22:13, 17.

He thought of the country, wild and unsettled, that had become his home, and he resolved that he would follow justice and fair play. Much as he wanted a part in the future of the West, he made up his mind that he would never deal dishonestly or take part in the violence around him.

He looked at his first crop; and, although the urge of the goldfields still drew him, he knew that the trail of gold would always be bloodied with violent acts and plagued with greed and deceit. He watched the gentle undulations of the green wheat and felt comforted.

Now reports reached Hell Gate of a new gold strike at Bannack. Elliot and his new friends rushed off to stake out claims. But Lisha, jealous for his wheat crop, stayed by his field. He and Elliot had bought the seed that spring for $10 a bushel. Now the price of wheat had dropped; still Lisha expected to get $6 a bushel for his crop.

He entered into his harvest with enthusiasm. He worked from dawn till dark. Day by day, he saw the standing wheat cut with scythes and hand bound in bundles, then stacked in shocks ready for threshing. Lisha helped his neighbors and finally, just before snow fell, he saw the last of his grain threshed and sold.

One day Lisha heard a man who had ridden into Hell Gate describe in an excited voice a later gold strike than any he had heard about. A man had started to grub out sagebrush for a cabin site. "And, you know, when he pulled up this here sagebrush, gold nuggets were sticking around among the roots."

With such sensational news drawing him, Lisha planned to join his brother in Bannack. A letter had come from Elliot describing the gold camp of Bannack as a friendly place with good neighbors and fine prospects.

Lisha took the trail that led south over the pass between Bitterroot Valley and Big Hole Basin and on to the Grasshopper "diggins" at Bannack. The winter had been mild and the snow not too deep, and early in January of 1863, Lisha reached Bannack.

Somehow the description Elliot had given of a friendly community didn't seem to fit the picture that met Lisha's gaze. He felt a peculiar uneasy worry; he eyed the knots of armed men in the streets with suspicion.

Lisha rode his horse down the street to the livery stable. "I'm looking for my brother, Elliot Rouse." He slid from his horse and faced the man at the livery stable. "Do you happen to know him?"

The man looked at him with sharp interest. "Son," he said, "people in this camp don't tell nobody who they are or what they want unless they're looking for trouble."

Lisha stared at the man and said nothing.

"Course, I can see you're new here. Look, kid, you just don't know who you can trust. I wanna keep you out of trouble." Lisha decided that he liked this man who was kind enough to give him a word of caution. "I don't know your brother, but I'll help you find him."

Lisha followed his new friend to Skinner's Saloon. "Any of you fellas know Elliot Rouse?" The man called out. The buzz of conversation ended.

"Who's that you're lookin' for?" a voice inquired.

"Elliot Rouse," Lisha spoke up.

"Yes, I know him." A man started toward him.

Lisha thanked the man from the livery stable and turned to the stranger. "I'm Elliot's brother, Lisha." He held out his hand.

"I'm John Bozeman and right proud to meet you." He shook Lisha's hand. "Let's have a drink, and I'll take you over to the place where your brother stays."

"Thanks, I don't drink." Lisha studied the strong, fine-looking young man.

"Don't drink, eh?" Bozeman looked surprised. "Wish I could let the stuff alone."

John led Lisha down the main street, and after walking a short distance, he stopped and pointed out the cabin where Elliot lived on the bank of Grasshopper Creek. Lisha thanked his guide and walked on to the little shack.

Elliot's welcome made up for the disappointment Lisha had begun to feel in Bannack. The brothers talked while Elliot built up a fire to warm Lisha's chilled body and to cook a hot supper.

"Everything's changed since I wrote you that letter." Elliot looked more stern and severe than ever. "The gold has brought hundreds of strangers into town, and more come every day." He explained that the gold claims and the work were not plentiful enough to satisfy all the men who had crowded into Bannack. The winter freeze had put a stop to placer mining. Men milled about the streets with nothing to occupy their minds but liquor and mischief.

"Do you see that camp over there?" Elliot pointed to a cluster of covered wagons. "One day last week while the campers warmed themselves at an outside fire, one of the town toughs fired a shot right into the midst of them."

"What excuse could he give for such behavior?"

"Said he thought they were Indians."

"I suppose they are emigrants that got here too late to find housing or work."

"Correct," Elliot went on. "Of course, there are still good men in the town. Trouble is, you don't know who you can trust." Same words the man at the livery stable had used, Lisha thought. "There seems to be a bunch of revolver-toting toughs who are organized, and they control the town by a bloody code."

"What do you mean?"

"I mean that if you cross one of them, they will gang up on you. You have to go along with them or they mark you for murder," Elliot explained. "If you want to save your hide, stay away from Skinner's Saloon. That's where the toughs hang out."

Lisha wondered if Elliot had decided to stay away from the saloon. He hoped so. His mind went to John Bozeman, the man he had met in Skinner's Saloon and who had directed him to Elliot's cabin. "What about that fellow Bozeman?"

"Bozeman is all right. I think the only reason he goes to the saloon is because he's from Georgia, and most of the fellas that hang out there are Confederates or Confederate sympathizers," Elliot continued. "Of course, their gang rule isn't confined to Skinner's Saloon. They have the upper hand in Bannack now."

Lisha had worked with rough men here in the West, but nothing had prepared him for the violence he found in Bannack. The wild, ungoverned lives of the miners, gamblers, ruffians, horse thieves, and robbers shocked him. Before he had been in town many days, he saw two young men ride away from Skinner's Saloon in a state of drunken frenzy. They began firing into one of the lodges in an Indian camp only a short distance from Yankee Flat, which lay across Grasshopper Creek and east of Elliot's cabin.

They returned to the saloon for a few more drinks and reinforcements. Then they returned to the Indian camp to "finish the job." They poured volley after volley into the Indian lodge with deadly effect. An Indian chief fell; so did a Frenchman who had come out to see what the shooting was about. A lame boy and a papoose were also carried out dead.

The miners became so enraged over this atrocity that they convened a miner's court, arrested the criminals, and tried them. Lisha expected the young desperadoes to hang for their crimes. But the jury, intimidated by the "gang," failed to ask for the death penalty and banished the offenders from town instead.

Throughout the rest of that winter, Lisha saw people killed almost daily with guns and knives.

Some good things happened in Bannack during those months. One of the best was the coming of Sidney Edgerton. He had been elected to Congress in 1858. Now, in 1863, he had accepted an appointment as chief justice of the newly organized Idaho Territory. On his way to Lewiston, he stopped in Bannack and found tremendous agitation for a division of the huge Idaho Territory. Idaho Territory at that time included what now makes up the states of Idaho, Montana, Wyoming, and the western parts of North and South Dakota.

The Sunday after Edgerton's arrival, Elliot and Lisha heard an orator climb into a covered wagon and deliver a most persuasive plea for a split of the vast Idaho Territory. They could see that Judge Edgerton was much affected. Citizens of Bannack and surrounding settlements met and chose Judge Edgerton to act as their agent in Washington, D.C., to secure a division of the territory.

"I shouldn't wonder if he gets it," Elliot said after the judge had left for the East.

"I think he will too. Did you see the gold buttons that Mrs. Edgerton

21

sewed onto the judge's coat? They couldn't help being convinced—those men in Washington. At least they will realize that Bannack is an important place."

"The Civil War makes gold important right now, I suppose," Elliot said.

A year later, Judge Edgerton came back from Washington with the good news that Idaho Territory had been divided. The eastern portion would be known as Montana Territory. On his way back, the judge was notified of his appointment as first governor of the new territory. Bannack became the first capital.

Meanwhile, two other persons rode into Bannack during the winter of 1862–63—a man named Henry Plummer and his friend Jack Cleveland. Within a month, the two quarreled and Plummer shot and killed his partner. He successfully pleaded self-defense. But the sheriff, Hank Crawford, had carried the dying Cleveland into his room to care for him in his own bed. Plummer had no way of knowing what Cleveland had said to the sheriff.

"You know, Plummer is trying to draw the sheriff into a gunfight," Elliot told Lisha one evening. "He's afraid Hank knows too much. He's afraid Cleveland may have talked before he died."

"Well, I think Hank's too smart for him even if Plummer is the fastest gun in the West," Lisha said with admiration.

A day or so later, Lisha saw Plummer hanging around the sheriff's meat market. Lisha felt sure that he hoped to catch the sheriff and shoot him, but then he saw that the sheriff had foiled Henry Plummer again. He had taken up a position across the street; and, taking deliberate aim, he shot Plummer in the right arm, thus ruining his marksmanship for a few weeks—or until he learned to shoot with his left hand.

"Why don't people stand up for the sheriff?" Lisha asked in disgust when he told Elliot about it. "They're too scared for their own lives, I suppose."

"Correct!" Elliot said. "Hank could have killed Plummer as easily as he shot him in the arm. The sheriff wants peace and order. He doesn't want to kill people."

During the next few days, the whole band of ruffians turned on the sheriff and made several attempts to kill him. When he fled for his life, they made Henry Plummer sheriff of Bannack.

# 4
# ALDER GULCH

Lisha had no taste for mining. The selfishness and greed of the gold seekers revolted him. He took a job as stable boy at Plummer's livery stable. He heard all sorts of rumors about his boss, but Lisha never made quick decisions for or against anyone. He admired Plummer for his strength, his marksmanship, and his ability to influence other men. After all, he had now become the law in Bannack. He held the sheriff's office.

One evening while Lisha worked about the livery stable, he heard some men discussing a heavy shipment of gold which had just come in by stage from the mines. A man named Buck Stinson said, "I don't think we'll have any trouble. The driver is just a young kid and should be easy to scare."

Lisha suspected that before morning the robber band would try to steal the gold. He kept his ears open and heard other scraps of talk and understood that the stage driver had hidden the gold in the manure pile behind the barn. The next morning, Lisha found the manure pitched all over the backyard. He knew then that the young driver had outwitted Buck Stinson and his fellow thieves.

As the days went by, Lisha began to see that Henry Plummer did not intend to enforce the law or protect the rights of Bannack's citizens. On the contrary, he shielded criminals and desperadoes. Lisha decided to give up his job with Plummer and began looking around for something else to do.

Elliot had become a close friend of John Bozeman. Lisha admired Bozeman and felt relieved that Elliot had attached himself to a good, substantial person. In some ways, the two had common interests. Both had left young families and come west to make a home to which they could bring their wives and children. Elliot had come from Minnesota, while Bozeman had left his family in Georgia. One a Union sympathizer and the other a strong Confederate, they did not let their political differences mar their friendship.

Bozeman bought a lot in Bannack, and now he hired Elliot to help him get out logs for a cabin. But as the days passed and the town became more violent and lawless while Plummer and his gang held control, Bozeman said one day, "I'm not going to finish this cabin. I won't bring my wife and children to Bannack." A few days later, he sold his lot and the logs for the cabin and set out with an old trail scout, John Jacobs, to find a new and shorter route for emigrants coming west to the goldfields in Montana.

Lisha saw the money from his wheat harvest dribbling away and knew he must find something profitable to do before it vanished. During his work at Plummer's livery stable, he had observed that merchandise freighted into the gold camps brought fabulous prices. Produce commanded any price the freighter could get for it. He saw one man sell ninety pounds of beans for $25.

He talked to Elliot. "Think I'll begin freighting. It looks like a gold mine to me."

Elliot took his pipe from his mouth and looked Lisha over with his stern dark eyes. "Freighting is a mighty tough job, Lish."

"Not too tough for me." Lisha had grown a little taller, but he knew now that he would never be tall like Elliot. "I'm sure I'll like freighting better than mining or being a stable boy."

"You know there's always the danger of Indians and road agents." Elliot put his pipe back in his mouth and talked around it. "You're not yet eighteen. I know you're wiry and quick, and you've got a way with animals; but"—he hesitated—"I just don't like the idea."

Lisha said nothing. He had secretly hoped that his brother would throw in with him. He knew that Elliot, out of work since Bozeman left, had begun to hang around the saloon again, and he'd seen other things he didn't like. If he could get Elliot out on the road away from the saloons and bad companions, he'd do better. He thought of Melissa and the little boys back in Minnesota and wondered when Elliot would ever be settled so he could bring them west. He wondered if Elliot ever wrote to Melissa, but he didn't ask.

"Well," Elliot said, "if your mind is made up, I know better than to try to change it."

Lisha sat looking at his brother. He wished Elliot had gone with John Bozeman to scout out that new trail. The trip would be dangerous enough, but not so dangerous as the saloons and the bad influences in Bannack. He wished that he could do something, but he decided that nothing was likely to turn Elliot from his wild ways.

Even before Lisha joined the caravan of freighters bound south for Salt Lake, Elliot got into serious trouble. He had been drinking and began to argue with Buck Stinson over some trifle. Buck, one of the most dangerous of the outlaws, threatened him.

A man came running out of the saloon and over to the spot where Lisha worked at getting his wagon ready for the Salt Lake trip. "Hurry, Lish! Elliot's in trouble!"

Lisha dropped his work, grabbed his gun, and ran to the saloon. At the door, he looked in and saw the other customers standing around Stinson and Elliot while the two sparred with one another, each trying to get the drop on the other. For the moment, Elliot seemed to have the advantage.

Stinson yelled, "Watch it, Rouse! Next time I'll get you for sure!"

Lisha calmly trained his gun on Buck Stinson. One of Stinson's pals touched the outlaw's sleeve, and Stinson turned to look straight down the barrels of Lisha's shotgun. He paled, dropped the argument, and left the saloon muttering curses.

The two brothers walked back to the cabin. "You can't stay here in Bannack any longer," Lisha told Elliot. "It's not only Buck Stinson that'll be gunning for you. Plummer and his whole gang of outlaws will have you marked."

Elliot dropped into a chair. He seemed a little dazed, and his speech came thick and harsh. "Guess you're right, Lish."

But still it did not seem to occur to Elliot that he might join Lisha on the trip to Salt Lake.

Another friend of the Rouse brothers, William Beall, lived in Bannack, and he, too, had no job. Elliot talked his situation over with Beall, and they decided to turn to produce raising. Turnips sold for twenty cents a pound and potatoes a dollar a pound. They knew that any garden produce they might raise would sell at a good price in the mining camps.

A few settlers had located in the Gallatin Valley to the northeast. Although they must travel quite a distance to reach the gold camps, they did not think of that as a handicap. They had found good fertile land there, and they talked about their fine prospects. Elliot, however, knew of other good farmland at Three Forks, the headwaters of the Missouri River.

Beall, an architect and carpenter by trade, liked the idea of leaving

Bannack to try gardening. "Tell you how we'll work it," he said to Elliot. "Lish will take oxen and the wagon and go to Salt Lake for seed. As soon as the weather permits, you and I will head for Three Forks and get some ground ready for planting."

"We'll have to fence too," Elliot reminded them, "otherwise the wild critters will eat everything."

With a lighter heart, Lisha joined the other bullwhackers in the caravan to Salt Lake. He intended to get seed potatoes and seeds of other vegetables he hoped would do well in the Montana climate. Then he would fill his wagon with other merchandise that he could freight to Bannack and sell at a profit.

The day Lisha had left Bannack, coffee sold for a dollar a pound and tea for three dollars a pound. So, in Salt Lake, he picked up a good supply of both commodities. A dealer offered him a bargain in dried apples, and he decided to take a chance on them.

Lisha finished his purchasing and loaded before the other freighters. Eager to get back in time to sow the crops at the right time, he, with a few other wagons, started back along the trail to the gold camps. He hazed his six head of oxen as fast as he dared. The heavy wagon could hold four tons of freight. The round trip from Bannack to Salt Lake and back took a month, and Lisha knew that he must dispose of his merchandise in the gold camps and then go on to Three Forks.

He reached Bannack without incident and sold his freight at an excellent profit. Then he hastened on to Three Forks, where he hoped Elliot and Beall would have land fenced, plowed, and ready for planting.

He found them hard at work. They had chosen land that could be irrigated from a stream, so their crops would not suffer for lack of water.

While the Rouse brothers and their partner worked at their planting, exciting news trickled into Three Forks. A large exploring expedition had left Bannack in two parties under the guidance of James Stuart and a half-breed scout, Louis Simmons. The two parties had planned to meet at the mouth of the Ruby River, but through a misunderstanding, they failed to make contact. The smaller group, led by Simmons, were captured by Indians and taken to their camp, then arraigned before their chief in a medicine lodge.

One of the men, Bill Fairweather, had a peculiar ability to handle poisonous snakes. On the way to the Indian camp, he had picked up two rattlesnakes and slipped them inside his shirt.

Now, while the Indians deliberated on what to do with their captives, Fairweather pulled out his two rattlesnakes. He did tricks with them and played with the writhing serpents in the most sinister manner.

Fairweather did more. He pulled up the sacred medicine bush that grew beside the lodge and struck the chief with it, at the same time flourishing his snakes with menacing gestures.

All the Indians in the medicine house seemed overcome with awesome terror. They decided that this white man's magic must be more powerful than their own. They returned the horses and other equipment which they had taken from the party and urged the white men to leave.

Simmons, the half-breed scout, perhaps impressed by Fairweather's show of magic, elected to remain with the Indians.

Reduced now to six men, the little party tried to find the way back to Bannack by a devious route in order to avoid any more attacks by Indians.

On May 26, they camped for the night in Alder Gulch, named for the alders that grew in abundance along the creek. Fairweather and Henry Edgar stayed in camp to guard the horses, cook the food, and wash the dishes while the other four men took a look along the canyon for signs of gold.

The horses grazed downstream farther than Fairweather thought safe, and he went to bring them back. Always alert for signs of gold, he noticed an outcropping of rimrock that struck him as interesting. He took the horses back to camp and brought Edgar back to have a look. Both of them brought picks and shovels.

They dug and washed three pans and found about forty-five cents worth of gold—free gold! By the time the other men returned, they had washed out $12.50 worth of gold.

During the next five days, the six men in the party staked out claims and panned $160 worth. As though carried by the spring winds, news of the fresh gold strike spread, with tremendous results. Hundreds of men headed for the new placer, each trying to outrun the other to stake a good claim. Almost overnight claims were staked out over a distance of twelve miles along the creek in Alder Gulch.

Within a week hundreds of tents, brush shelters, and rude cabins sprang up. Many men did not even take time to build shelters but slept on the ground beside their "diggins." Still more came, and at the end of three months, the population of Alder Gulch reached an estimated ten thousand. Thus Virginia City came into being. By the end of the year, ten million dollars in gold would be taken from the mines in Alder Gulch.

To the Rouse brothers, working from dawn to dark in their gardens and fields, the strike in Alder Gulch meant a nearer and perhaps even better market for the produce they were growing. Lisha watched Elliot for signs of gold fever, but he and William Beall both stuck by the land.

Later that summer, John Bozeman came through Three Forks. He had left Laramie on July 6, 1863, as one of two guides for an emigrant train of forty-one wagons. When they were fourteen days out on the trail to the gold camps, one hundred and fifty Indians of the Cheyenne and Sioux nations met the train and urged them to turn back. "If you turn back now, no harm will come to you," the chiefs said. "If you continue on, there will be great destruction. No wagon train shall pass through our country."

After much discussion, the wagon master decided to turn back. Bozeman, much disappointed, left the wagon train three days later with ten men. They struck out for the Montana mines.

They were not prepared for the long and dangerous journey. They ran out of both food and ammunition. But Bozeman's courage and ingenuity saved them. They snared small game and ate wild berries. They moved with furtive stealth to escape detection by hostile Indians. They reached the Yellowstone River and followed it for some distance, then left it (at the spot where the city of Livingston now stands) and continued along a well-worn Indian trail over a mountain pass which the Indians called Yellowstone Pass.

They descended into the Gallatin Valley, which Bozeman described as rich and fertile beyond anything he had seen. From there they pushed on to Three Forks. Bozeman explained that he would go from Three Forks down the Jefferson River to Point of Rocks and on west to Bannack. Lisha saw that he had mapped his route with care so that others could follow it. (Later it became known as the Bozeman Trail.)

During that summer, the Rouse brothers made trips to the goldfield to dispose of their garden produce. Rabbits ate their peas and lettuce. No fence could keep them out. But beets, turnips, and beans excelled anything they had ever seen before, and the crop of potatoes proved excellent.

Elliot took the light wagon and transported the garden produce to

Virginia City, Nevada City, and Bannack. He sold it at great profit. For the first time since they had come West, fortune smiled on the two brothers.

Then they discovered that feuds in the gold camps were never forgotten. On one of Elliot's trips into Bannack where Henry Plummer still held the sheriff's office, the outlaw invited him into the saloon to drink with him.

One of Elliot's old friends warned him, "Plummer hasn't forgotten your fight with Buck Stinson. You said something that day that made him think you knew about his criminal record. You're a marked man, Elliot. He's out to kill you!"

In spite of the warning, Elliot went into the saloon with Plummer for a drink; but when the sheriff tried to draw on him, he found himself looking into the barrel of Elliot's gun. "Keep your hands off that gun, Plummer, or you're as good as dead!" Elliot spoke in a cool, commanding voice.

Plummer withdrew his hand. "Never mind, Rouse, I'll get you yet. You're a mighty game cock as long as you've got the drop on me."

Everyone in Bannack knew Plummer's reputation as a gunman. Everyone knew that he had already murdered seven or eight men by using the same trick he had tried to work on Elliot—inviting them to have a drink with him and then shooting them dead as they stood at the bar.

When Elliot got back to Three Forks, he related his experience to Lisha and Beall. "You fellas will have to peddle the vegetables in the gold camps from now on. It's too dangerous for me in Bannack."

So Lisha and Beall hauled the produce until the last load in the fall. This time the wagon, weighted down with potatoes, seemed too much for one man to handle alone, so Elliot went along with Beall. He also intended, on this last trip, to collect several accounts from merchants with whom he had left produce on consignment.

Lisha watched them out of sight and thought how much more wholesome their situation seemed to be now. He even hoped that Elliot would soon settle down, build a house, and send for his family. Elliot seldom mentioned Melissa and the children anymore.

# 5
## "SHALL I KILL THEM BOTH?"

On his late fall trip to Bannack with their big load of potatoes, Elliot and his partner, William Beall, took great care to avoid any encounter with Plummer and his gang of cutthroats. They worked hard all day disposing of their potatoes and collecting money due them from the town's merchants.

Near sundown they finished. "I think we'd better not stay in Bannack tonight," Elliot said. "I know where there's an old abandoned cabin a few miles out of town. We can spend the night there and slip away early in the morning. That way we'll avoid any trouble."

Beall agreed, and they drove their light wagon out in the direction of the cabin.

"There's a light!" Elliot tightened the reins. "Wonder who can be staying there."

The two men decided to knock and find out if they might shelter there for the night.

When Elliot saw the man who came to the door and looked beyond him into the lighted room, he realized that they had walked into a gathering of road agents, members of Plummer's band of outlaws. He recognized several of them.

Elliot thought fast. He and Beall could not turn back to Bannack. To go on would be certain death, for he knew the man at the door had recognized him. These men had a score to settle for their leader. Elliot knew that he must deal wisely with a deadly situation, or both he and Beall would die.

"We planned to camp here tonight," he explained in a calm voice. "We didn't know the cabin would already be full."

"Come right in. Plenty of room for us all. Put up your horses and come in." The man flung the door wide.

Beall took bedding from the wagon and followed the man into the cabin. Elliot unhitched the team, fed them, watered them, and bedded them down. Then he turned toward the cabin with a sick feeling at the pit of his stomach. The peril of the situation almost overwhelmed him. Only cool thinking

30

would give him and his partner any chance at all. This episode might well write the conclusion to the feud between Buck Stinson and Elliot Rouse.

Beall had taken a room not occupied by the road agents and had thrown down their bedrolls. He had everything ready when Elliot came in. They blew out their lantern, and Elliot got into bed. "Come on to bed, Beall," he said. "The law of the road agents is that you must not kill a man while he is a guest under your roof. Don't you know that?"

Beall said he did not feel at all sleepy. He took a position behind the rough wooden door and watched the men through the cracks. In each hand he held a loaded gun. He put the bag of money they had gathered that day in Bannack under his knees.

The men in the other room sat up most of the night playing cards. Once Beall heard part of their conversation. Then he knew that he had been right not to trust any robbers' rule of courtesy. They might never leave this place alive. One of the card-players said, "Shall I kill them both or just the one?"

Beall strained his ears to hear the reply, but raucous laughter drowned out further talk. He kept his guns cocked and ready and saw the man who had asked the question leave the room. What sort of murder weapon had he gone to fetch?

Now only a short time remained before morning. Elliot and Beall rose early, dressed, and went out. They found that two chickens had been prepared for breakfast. Then Beall realized what victims the men had planned to murder in the night.

When the partners had hitched their team to the wagon and prepared to continue their journey, one of the Plummer gang, whom the others called "Red," asked if he could ride along with them. "I've got business down at the ranch."

Elliot understood him to mean Plummer's ranch, which the people of Bannack called "Robber's Roost."

He had expected some such maneuver. He realized that the battle of wits had begun. His life and Beall's depended on the winner. With studied coolness, Elliot said, "Of course. Come right along."

He drove the team while Beall kept his eye on their passenger. As soon as they got out of sight of the other road agents, Beall slipped his hand down over his gun. "If any road agents try to pick a fight with us, there'll be one or two fewer of them."

Red turned and looked at the gun in Beall's hand. He seemed to catch the meaning of what he saw.

The road had been muddy the day before but had frozen during the night, and the wagon bumped over the trail at a slow crawling pace. Elliot heard voices. Just as he had expected, three or four horsemen came into view. His hand went to his own gun. Plummer's gang for sure!

His apprehension mixed with determination as he saw them spur their horses forward. Then he recognized their leader—John Bozeman.

Elliot's caution exceeded his relief, although he had never in all his life been so glad to see any person. He drew Bozeman aside and explained the desperate situation and how they had spent the night in the cabin with Plummer's cutthroats.

Even while they talked, three of Plummer's men rode into view. They had evidently been following the wagon and waiting for a signal from Red.

"Hey, fellas," Red called to his friends, "what about a ride over to the ranch?" He leaped out of the wagon and mounted behind one of the other riders, and they all galloped away.

As soon as the sound of hoof beats had faded in the distance, Elliot, Beall, Bozeman, and his companions held a conference. They tried to devise some plan to foil the road agents, for all of them knew that the robbers had not abandoned their plans.

Beall scratched his head. "What if you fellows ride along with us back to Virginia City, we can leave the wagon there and ride our own horses over the home trail."

Everyone agreed on this plan. The two partners reached Three Forks safely and told the story to Lisha. "Plummer is getting bolder all the time. Bannack is being strangled by his band of murdering thieves."

Lisha proposed to undertake another freighting trip to Salt Lake City. He had got a taste of freighting. He enjoyed selecting likely merchandise and selling it to eager buyers in the gold camps. He joined a caravan bound for the Mormon city on the southern desert.

On this trip, some of the bullwhackers aroused the ire of several peaceable travelers. Resentment of ill treatment flared into vengeance, and half the drivers were killed by friends of the wronged men. Lisha, as usual, had maintained a tight-lipped silence, so he escaped the massacre.

Shaken and saddened, he loaded his wagons and returned to the gold towns. He meditated all the way on the fate of his fellow drivers. Again, an eternity in hell hardly seemed a suitable punishment for those rough, thoughtless young bullwhackers who had already suffered violent deaths. He tried to shut the question from his mind. He felt sure there must be a God. Everywhere he looked the wonders of nature insisted on a higher Divine Power. But what kind of God could He be? He must be more cruel and fierce than any man who had ever lived.

Lisha pulled his freight into Bannack, turned his oxen out to graze, and collected his horse from the livery stable. That night he slept in a hotel.

In the morning, he took his horse from the stable and rode out to find his oxen. An acquaintance hailed him. "The vigilantes have hung Henry Plummer!" the man said. "They got Buck Stinson and Ned Ray too."

"Vigilantes!" Lisha, startled, slid down from his horse. "What do you mean by vigilantes? And Plummer executed?" His mind reeled. When he had left Bannack late the year before, Plummer had been secure in his office as sheriff. "Man—" He grabbed the front of his friend's coat. "When did this happen?"

"It started with George Ives." The man seemed bursting with excitement. "A few days ago, he murdered young Tiebalt, that sixteen-year-old kid that worked for some of the miners."

Lisha had seen young Tiebalt, but Ives he knew well. George Ives, a tall blue-eyed boy with fair hair, handsome as a prince, and he'd come from a fine family back in Wisconsin. He remembered the magnificent horse Ives used to ride into town to visit the saloons. Sometimes he backed his mount through glass store windows and rode away laughing. Yes, Ives had gone the way of the saloon and the road agents.

"Well, they tried Ives in a people's court in Virginia City with a jury of twenty-four miners. The judge sat in a wagon, and the jury sat in a half circle by a big log fire. It was mighty cold, you see. The trial lasted over two days, and hundreds of men came. All the decent citizens demanded that Ives be executed, and all the thugs and gunmen told what terrible things they'd do if anyone harmed a hair of George Ives's head. They all had guns and flourished them around." The man paused for breath and then went on.

"Last night they had the scaffold all ready and Ives on the box with a rope around his neck. Hundreds of people cried out in protest. Then Nelson Story stepped forward—a brave man, that Nelson Story. He called out in a mighty voice, 'Men, do your duty!' The click of a hundred gunlocks was

33

heard as the guards leveled their weapons on the crowd and someone kicked the box from under Ives's feet."

The man went on to tell how just before Ives was hanged, he had made a complete confession. He had named Henry Plummer and thirty members of his organized gang of road agents. The men of the gold camps did not wait till morning, but organized immediately for action. They dragged Plummer and two other desperadoes from their beds and hanged them before they realized that Ives had informed on them.

Lisha got back on his horse and rode out to the draw where the execution had taken place. Sure enough, there in the early January dawn, the three bodies dangled from a scaffold that Plummer himself had erected.

Lisha sat and contemplated them for a long time. All these men and the others whom the vigilantes were pouncing on today had been young and full of selfish ambition yesterday. Now only pitiful corpses remained. Again, the question thundered in Lisha's mind. Where had these men gone? Were they in hell? Would they burn forever and ever as the preachers said? He shook his head and turned away. Even though the Plummer gang had killed over a hundred people and committed many robberies, Lisha could hardly see that everlasting hellfire could be a suitable punishment.

The vigilantes acted with incredible swiftness. The respectable citizens of the gold camps had endured as much as they could bear. Patience had been exhausted. The vigilantes became pursuers, accusers, judges, jury, and executioners. The criminals had no defense against their vengeance.

Lisha didn't have much luck disposing of his freight that day. People crowded in from everywhere to look at the dead road agents and to recount their crimes. Sickened and confused, he decided to drive on to Virginia City. There he found that the vigilantes had executed five more outlaws. He stood in an unfinished store building and saw the bodies still hanging from the exposed beams.

"One got away," someone in the crowd said. "Bill Hunter."

At last Lisha sold his load of rock salt at a good profit and drove north to meet Elliot and Beall at Three Forks. He got there in time to assist in the capture of Bill Hunter.

# 6
# A TOWN IS BORN

Swift punishment fell on Bill Hunter as it had on all the others the vigilantes captured. Other questionable characters fled the country, and peace descended at last on the gold camps.

Lisha found his brother and William Beall excited about a proposed move into the rich eastern section of the Gallatin Valley. "John Bozeman thinks the eastern Gallatin has much better soil than Three Forks," Elliot said.

"So we went over to take a look," Beall added, "and we've found just what we want."

"Only drawback is that the trails of several Indian tribes cross right where we want to take up land." Elliot turned his stern look on his brother. "We'll have to bring in lots of settlers. If there are enough of us, we can defend ourselves."

They also related how they had taken a load of root vegetables into Virginia City and met John Bozeman. He had told them that he intended to bring a wagon train over the Bozeman Trail.

"Yes, and he wants us to take up land and start a town in the place we looked at. He's already drawn a diagram of the town plan."

They brought the plan out. Lisha could see that many settlers were coming from the East. The gold strikes and the virgin land drew them, while behind them the Civil War raged and pushed them west. The gold fields would play out, but the rich soil would remain.

Early in July, Elliot and Beall took up claims of one hundred sixty acres each, and they located an equal acreage for John Bozeman. They hoped the Gallatin Valley might prove one of the most desirable places in the West.

While Elliot and Beall hauled logs from the mountains and began building cabins, Lisha planned to continue his profitable business of freighting.

On July 6, Jim Bridger arrived with a wagon train, and John Jacobs came in a few days later with another. When Bozeman arrived with his wagon train a month later, Elliot joined him in visiting around at the emigrants' wagons. The two used all their charm to persuade the westbound travelers to settle right here in the Gallatin. "The soil is rich beyond belief, the water good and abundant," Elliot explained over and over again in his most convincing tones.

"It stands right at the gate of the mountains," Bozeman added, "where all the tenderfeet come in with their golden fleeces ready to be clipped."

The two promoters offered choice corner lots and even free lots to those who would start businesses. They induced two men, McAdow and Cover, to build a flour mill. They attracted many others who paused to listen and even offered to build homes for the new arrivals.

A general-merchandise store established by a man named Wilson added to the town's prestige, yet the town had not been named, and a citizens' committee met to choose a name. They could think of no other name so suitable as Bozeman. They all admired the daring young adventurer who had scouted and mapped new trails, had outwitted Indians and outlaws numberless times, and had even now, this end of July 1864, brought in a train of six hundred wagons. So the new town became Bozeman.

The new settlers dug irrigation ditches and planted wheat fields and gardens. Young orchards began to grow, and lush pastures fenced in livestock. The first school opened in 1865, and the town took on a substantial quality. More settlers came to swell the numbers of people in the Gallatin.

Lisha, now nearly twenty and an experienced trader and freighter among the gold camps in Montana, made a new friend, Billy Lee.

Cousin of the Confederate general, Robert E. Lee, Billy had trained to be a soldier. Although still a youth, he proved a blessing to the settlers in Bozeman during their frequent clashes with the Indians.

The two friends, convinced of Bozeman's bright future, took up squatters' claims east of the new town. They chose a location where the deep, rich soil could be irrigated from Bear Creek, and the two dug a canal that brought the water right to their building site.

"I don't expect to find anything better this side of Paradise," Lisha told Billy as they dug ditches, prepared their land for crops, and built log cabins.

A constant threat to the horses, the Crow Indians hung on the edges of the new settlement and stole whatever they could take. The men in Bozeman complained to the Indian Agency, but nothing came of it, and the Crows went on stealing horses.

Although the Crows were nearest to the town, the Sioux presented the greater danger. More warlike than the thieving Crows, they wanted other things like scalps and revenge.

One day word ran through the town that a war party of Sioux had been discovered advancing toward the settlement. With courageous leaders like John Bozeman and Billy Lee, they met the Sioux warriors where the trail crossed the divide and turned them back.

Now Indian troubles multiplied. About a mile south of Bozeman, an ancient Indian trail crossed the valley in an easterly course and made a beeline for what the Indians called Yellowstone Pass. Since Bozeman had scouted and mapped the trail, the settlers called it Bozeman Pass. Along Bozeman Trail and over Bozeman Pass flowed the great tide of emigrants from the East. Wagon wheels cut into the age-old trail, and the Indian tribes of the Northwest resented the intrusion.

For hundreds of years, their ancestors had used this route to travel from the Upper Columbia Basin east to the buffalo hunting grounds along the Yellowstone River. They determined that the white men, even though they came in frightening numbers, should not dispossess them of their ancient hunting grounds and their legal rights.

On the other hand, the settlers on the rich land determined that nothing should take their dearly bought right to live in Montana Territory.

The government built forts along the Bozeman Trail: Fort Reno, Fort Phil Kearney, Fort C. F. Smith, and Fort Ellis.

Although under treaty rights, the settlers had no business trespassing on the Indians' ancient trails and their buffalo hunting grounds, the men in the new settlements were ready to defy the Indians, the army, and anything else in order to establish and defend their homes.

Another intrepid pioneer came to settle in Bozeman, Nelson Story. Lisha remembered at once the report of his part in the execution of George Ives. Story had made a fortune in the gold camps, and now he came to the flourishing settlement in the Gallatin Valley intending to go into the cattle business. In spite of Indian troubles and the army's refusal to give him protection, Nelson Story decided to bring a herd of longhorn cattle from Texas.

Lisha and Billy Lee saw Story start off and wondered if he would ever make it through hundreds of miles of hostile Indian territory. "If anyone can do it, Nelson Story can," Lisha said.

"Yes, he knows the risks he's taking, and he's got the money to hire good men and arm them with the best weapons." Billy Lee looked so wistful that Lisha knew his friend would like nothing better than a chance to join Nelson Story's adventure.

Months passed, and one day in 1869, word flashed through the town that Nelson Story and his herd of longhorns had reached a spot on the eastern side of Bozeman Pass where he intended to set up a cattle camp with his six hundred longhorns. When Nelson himself rode into Bozeman, everyone crowded around him to hear of his trek. They saw that the cowboys with him carried Winchester rifles or Colt revolvers.

Story explained about their struggles against wind, rain, and dust, their fights with Indians, and their hardships because of water shortage. "I knew I could do it," he said. "I knew that if I hired capable men and equipped them with the best weapons, and we all pushed through with dogged determination, we would make it; and we did."

For weeks the people of Bozeman told and retold Nelson Story's remarkable exploit. He had done the impossible and done it with a flourish. Billy Lee, fascinated by such a courageous man, went to work in Story's cattle camp over the other side of the pass.

Tom Cover, partner in the Cover-McAdow Flour Milling Company of Bozeman, engaged Lisha Rouse to make a trip with John Bozeman to Fort C. F. Smith on the Big Horn River to take orders for flour. Lisha looked forward to the journey because he always enjoyed John Bozeman's company, and he would get to see Billy Lee at Nelson Story's cattle camp.

Just before they were to start, a minor breakdown occurred at the mill, and Tom Cover decided to make the trip himself and leave Lisha to do the repair job. Lisha watched the two ride off and felt sharp disappointment over missing such an adventure.

A few days later, some men rode into town with the terrible news: "John Bozeman is dead!"

"What happened?"

"Killed by thieving Indians!"

"And Tom Cover?"

"Wounded!"

The two men had spent their first night out at Nelson Story's cattle camp. Bozeman, usually so daring and confident, told his friends that he had a premonition that he would not come back from this trip alive.

During the night, Indians drove off a number of horses, but Billy Lee and Mitch Boyer, a famous Indian scout, pursued them and recovered all the horses but one pony.

The following morning, Bozeman and Tom Cover went on their way toward Fort Smith. They camped to eat their midday meal in a shady place beside a small creek. Five Indians approached them leading a pony—the one Story's men had not recovered. Both men thought the Indians were friendly Crows. Yet Cover warned Bozeman not to let them come too near. Bozeman held fire while Cover went to saddle his horse, leaving his gun on the ground.

Suddenly, one of the Indians whipped out his gun and shot Bozeman. He lunged at the Indians, and they fired again. He fell dead. The first bullet had pierced his heart. Cover ran for his gun, but the Indians shot and wounded him. Then they made off with the horses.

Cover wandered about in a daze all the rest of that day and the following night. The next morning he stumbled into Nelson Story's cattle camp.

No one in the settlement took Bozeman's death so hard as Elliot. Immediately, he set out with a few friends for the Yellowstone, intending to bring John Bozeman's body back to town for burial.

The men came back a few days later without the body. Elliot explained that the weather and the terrible road conditions made it impossible to bring the body back at that time. They had buried Bozeman there on the Yellowstone. Later, they would remove him to the town that bore his name.*

Often in the days that followed, as Lisha shared the grief his brother Elliot felt over losing his best friend, he thought about the circumstances that had prevented his going along with Bozeman on the day the Indians killed him. Had a Higher Power ordered the events of his life and prevented him from making that fateful trip?

Shortly after Bozeman's death, Fort Ellis was activated for protection of settlers in the Gallatin Valley. Now the United States Government began to negotiate a new treaty with the Indians. More than a fourth of Montana with much of Dakota and Wyoming was ceded to the Indians. They received guns and other supplies as an inducement to sign the treaty.

---

* Two years later, Nelson Story brought the remains to Bozeman for burial in Sunset Hills Cemetery on Elliot Rouse's property. Finally, the plot was purchased by the city of Bozeman and made a municipal cemetery. Story erected a splendid monument over the grave, which one may see today.

Under its terms, the government closed off Bozeman Pass and deactivated Fort C. F. Smith, which had protected it. Emigration almost ceased. Settlers on the east side of Bozeman Pass had no protection from Indian attack. The front door leading to the new settlements in Montana had slammed shut. The guns and ammunition which the government had given the Indians for buffalo hunting, the tribes now turned on the white settlers. Bozeman found its position cramped and perilous.

Now dark and bloody days followed in a procession of horse stealing, attacks on settlers, and desperate revenge, especially from the cattlemen, who did not take meekly the plundering of their herds or the loss of their horses. The days of danger and unrest stretched into years.

Lisha went out with one party to locate a band of trouble-making Indians. His duty was to find the enemy and determine their number and how best to approach them. He found the Indians a much larger and stronger force than the officer in charge had anticipated. He feared to attack, and Lisha found himself in a retreat pursued by raging savages.

He, with other scouts, fought a delaying action to cover the retreat. Lisha noticed a boy on a white mule who seemed unable to keep up with the other soldiers. He worried about the boy. Suddenly, an arrow struck the mule in the rump, and immediately he flashed ahead to take his place at the head of the fleeing settlers. The boy waved his arms and flung back a frantic call, "Hurry up, or we'll all be killed!"

Lisha's land had been taken for Fort Ellis, so he lived with Elliot in the town of Bozeman; but he frequently took his ox wagons on long freighting trips to Salt Lake City.

Lisha always found plenty of excitement when he pulled into Bozeman after a freighting trip. People crowded around to tell him what had happened while he had been away and to hear news of the outside world even though it might already be a month old.

One summer day in 1870, Lisha found special news waiting for him. "Lisha, d'you know Elliot is going to get married?"

"Well, you don't say!" Lisha took care of his freight and wagon and hurried home. "What's this I hear about you, Elliot?"

Elliot tried to act unconcerned, but a flush rose in his cheeks, and under Lisha's persistent questioning he admitted that he expected to marry Susan Hitchcock.

Lisha knew Susan. Everyone in town knew her for a fine young woman. She would make a thrifty and devoted wife, Lisha felt sure. "Well, Elliot, all I can say is that Susan's a wonderful girl, and I hope your wandering days are over. Maybe you can settle down now and make a proper home."

Elliot said nothing, and Lisha went outside to walk the street and think about the ten years that had passed since he and his brother had left Elliot's first wife, Melissa, and his two small boys in Minnesota. He knew that Elliot's neglect had destroyed his first marriage. Elliot had fallen in with bad company when they came west, and he had followed the loose ways of his companions. Gradually, Elliot had lost interest in Melissa, and the marriage had ended in divorce. Too bad!

On Elliot's wedding day, Lisha watched the ceremony. Susan in her white wedding dress looked up into Elliot's face in complete love and trust. The justice of the peace interrupted Lisha's thoughts by saying, "If any man can show just cause why they may not be joined together in holy matrimony, let him speak now or forever hold his peace."

Looking at Susan's radiant face, Lisha resolved to "forever hold his peace."

Elliot had been one of Bozeman's founders. He had worked hard to bring about his dream of a secure home in the West. Now he had become one of the prosperous businessmen of the town. Lisha hoped that Susan's influence would settle Elliot down and make him into a better man.

That winter a letter came from Melissa. She urged Elliot to come and get his two boys. She had tried to bring them up the best she could, but she felt that they needed a father's care. "Perhaps now that you have a home of your own, you will want your two sons." She added that she loved them dearly and would miss them, but for their own good she had decided that they should go to their father.

In April, Elliot prepared for his trip back to Michigan, where Melissa now lived. Susan stayed home in Bozeman. She had already taken her brother's two children to care for, and she and Elliot had adopted her sister's daughter, Ida. Lisha saw that Susan looked forward with eagerness to having Elliot's two boys to love and care for. A generous woman with a big heart— bigger than most, he thought. A bride of only a few months, she already had welcomed five children. He gave Susan all the help he could while Elliot was away on his trip east.

# 7

# "I'M GOING TO GET A BIBLE"

Elliot did not hurry. He took time to visit his sister Helen whom he had not seen for sixteen years, and he spent some time with her family.

Letters came back telling how Elliot had talked with Helen and her husband night after night, telling them of the rich possibilities of the Gallatin Valley. In the end, Maynard Randall, Helen's husband, decided to take his wife and five children west. He would come back to Bozeman with Elliot. They would travel by train to Corrine, Utah, the nearest railway approach to the Gallatin Valley.

Lisha met the travelers at the railway stop with a covered wagon, which would be the most comfortable way to transport them to Montana. He rejoiced to see his older sister again, and he welcomed the children with delight. Elliot's two boys had grown to be fine fellows. Melissa had done an excellent job of training them, and Lisha could see how proud Elliot was of his sons.

The children swarmed over the covered wagon shouting with excitement over the prospects of adventurous days on the trail to the Gallatin. Lisha and the other three adults did not share their enthusiasm. October had come already, and the days grew chilly. Nights could be uncomfortably cold. Although Susan had sent along every comfort she could think of, the long journey was bound to be difficult.

Early on their homeward trip, they stopped at the cabin of a squaw man (white man married to an Indian woman). They asked if they might warm themselves and make a pot of tea. Although they furnished the tea, he charged them five dollars for the use of his hot water. The new arrivals from the East made a few remarks about the hospitality of the West, which Lisha thought appropriate. "But just wait till we get to Bozeman," he said.

The glamour of the wagon trip faded as the days went by, and all the travelers wished for better roads and better weather. Then an early winter storm blanketed the land with snow. They overtook a flock of sheep, and Lisha drove close behind them. The sheep packed down the snow and made traveling easier. They reached Bozeman in November of 1871 and found such a welcome as would have warmed the heart of anyone. Lisha blessed Susan in his heart a hundred times for all the kindness she heaped on the weary family of his sister Helen and on Elliot's two boys.

In 1872, the Northern Pacific Railroad sent surveying parties across Bozeman Pass and down the Yellowstone. Hope sprang up in Bozeman, only to be struck down when the people learned that the Indians had successfully frightened the surveyors away.

During these troubled years after Lisha lost his land, he often made freighting trips to Salt Lake City. He also made several journeys north to Fort Benton hauling supplies and other freight. He spent long lonely hours on the trail, driving his plodding oxen over the wearying miles. During these trips, he had plenty of time to think—to review his experiences in the West.

He remembered Joseph Slade, who had first hired him as a helper on his stagecoach line. He had been a good man then, but now Lisha heard the story of Slade's final years. Like many other young men in the West, Slade took to drink. Though he was a good man when sober, liquor turned him into a devil. Finally, one day, crazed with drink, he defied arrest and threw a whole town into an uproar. He was holding up a store with a derringer in each hand when the vigilantes apprehended him and gave him one hour to live. When that hour expired, Joseph Slade expired with it.

Strange, mused Lisha, that nearly all the bad men hunted by the vigilantes had come from good homes. But in the West, they had yielded to evil influences and become as wild and reckless as savages. He thought how his brother, Elliot, had drifted from his home training and become antireligious. He hoped that now with Susan, Elliot could have a better life.

The citizens of Bozeman had built a church, but few people attended it except for funerals or weddings. Lisha felt no inclination to interest himself in any church.

Thinking these thoughts, he saw that he was approaching the stage station at Bird Tail. He noticed a fresh mound of earth beside the trail and turned in to the station to ask who had been buried in the fresh grave.

"A girl who lived here at Bird Tail," the man in charge told him. "She caught smallpox from a passenger going through on the stage. Although she got well, the smallpox disfigured her face terribly."

"So that's why—"

"Well, indirectly. She looked so hideous that her people hid all mirrors and never allowed her to see herself. She had become engaged to a fine young man. He planned to come in on the stage last week. Just before the time for him to arrive, the girl came out to meet him. Someone told her to go back in, that she would frighten the passengers. She did go back—insisted on seeing a mirror. She looked at her horribly altered features, took a gun, and shot herself."

Lisha climbed back into his wagon and drove on, pondering this tragedy. Just a young girl barely eighteen! And she had taken her own life. Because she had yielded to a moment of despondency, God would burn her in hell for all eternity. She must suffer the torments of the damned forever.

The more Lisha thought about it, the more angry he became. He began to talk in a fierce loud voice using powerful words. His oxen began to hurry at a faster and faster pace. But Lisha did not bring the bullwhip down on their backs; he just talked on.

He had once heard a preacher say that the punishment of the wicked was for the benefit of the saints. He couldn't imagine what kind of saint would be benefited by hearing the shrieks of the damned throughout unending millenniums.

"I'm going to get a Bible," he shouted at the oxen and the empty trail. "There must be an answer to this question, and I intend to find it."

On a beautiful June day in 1873, Lisha rode past the cemetery where he could see the splendid monument erected to the memory of John Bozeman. How he wished that Bozeman could have lived to see the town now. He turned his eyes north and east where granite peaks marked the course of the creek and Bridger Canyon. He liked to think of Bridger and Bozeman, courageous men, both of them. They had lived tough, fearless lives. Somehow he felt kin to them.

He reined in his horse and headed for the fort, where he intended to join Kelly, an army scout. They had been ordered to carry a dispatch from Colonel Gibbon to Major Freeman, who was on maneuvers east of Bozeman Pass.

The Indians had grown more and more defiant. Any white man who ventured into the Yellowstone Valley east of Bozeman Pass ran the risk of being scalped. Lisha ran his hands through his thick, dark hair. "I'd sure hate to lose it that way," he said aloud.

At the fort he found Kelly, and together they went to Colonel Gibbon's office. The colonel handed them the papers in a sealed envelope and showed them, on a map, the location of Major Freeman's camp.

They mounted their horses and rode east toward Kelly's Canyon. Two miles north of the fort they entered the foothills and followed an old wagon road used by emigrants until the government closed Bozeman Pass. This road had been the ancient buffalo trail of the Nez Percé and the Flatheads—Columbia River Indians. The Blackfeet also claimed it, those Ishmaelites of the plains whose hand was against all other men, red or white.

Lisha knew that he and Kelly would need to use all their alert precaution in traveling over this disputed territory. The Indians exerted their utmost cunning to prevent wolvers (men who trapped wolves for their pelts) and any other white men from crossing it.

The two scouts rode across the pass without incident and descended to the big bend of the Yellowstone River. After reaching the river, they chose to travel by the back hill country which, they reasoned, would give them better cover. The Indian scouts who watched the regularly traveled road would be less likely to spot them. A little beyond the mouth of the Shields River, they camped for the night.

They picketed their horses, built no fire, but ate a cold supper. Lisha would stand guard the first half of the night and Kelly the last half.

Lisha walked to a little knoll just above the spot where the horses were picketed. He listened to the night sounds. A coyote howled in the distance. Others joined him until the eerie chorus of the Western plains pierced the night. Lisha felt sleepy. He looked down and tried to see the horses and could just make out their shadowy forms against the plain.

Suddenly, one of the horses lifted his head and whinnied. Lisha listened, wide awake now. Would some other horse answer? He heard nothing. Then the horse neighed again. Lisha hurried down to waken Kelly, but Kelly had already heard. "Sounds like we may expect visitors," he whispered.

"I'll get the horses in," Lisha volunteered.

While Lisha brought the horses, Kelly found his saddle and as soon as Lisha came up with the horses, Kelly dropped his saddle on his mount and drew up the cinch. Lisha stooped to pick up his saddle when about a dozen Indians seemed to rise up out of the prairie. Lisha turned to leap on his horse, but Kelly's mount, in wild rush to get away, knocked him down.

Before Lisha could get to his feet, his own horse bolted. A gun spoke and then another. Lisha heard Kelly's Colt respond and felt a bullet tear through his shoulder.

An Indian flashed in for Lisha's scalp. Though wounded, he fought like a tiger, but the Indians outnumbered and overwhelmed him. He did not lose his scalp, but he lost consciousness. When he came to himself, daylight flooded the valley. His Indian captors had bound his hands. He knew himself to be a prisoner of the terrible Sioux. His left arm and shoulder throbbed with pain, and he felt dizzy.

When the Indians saw that he had wakened, they gave him a drink of water and told him to get on his horse. Someone had caught and saddled it.

Every muscle in his body ached. The Indians must have beaten him until he lapsed into unconsciousness. Riding hurt his arm and shoulder; but as time passed, he seemed to get used to the misery and felt able to bear it. He thought of Kelly and hoped that he had escaped and would tell the army about the encounter.

All that day the Indians and their captive rode, and then they camped for the night. The following day, they reached the Indian camp. Lisha estimated the number of lodges at about thirty. Word quickly spread that a white prisoner had been brought into the village. Black eyes peered out of the tepees, and dark faces stared at him. His captors led him at once to the chief's lodge. Here they told him to dismount and enter. Already a large crowd of curious Indians had gathered.

Lisha looked from one face to another, and he saw that none looked friendly. Even the little children showed plainly their hatred for the white man.

Inside the council lodge, the leading men of the village formed a circle. The Indians pushed Lisha into the center of the circle. He longed for someone to dress his wounded shoulder. The pain seemed to grow worse and worse, but he said nothing. He could expect no pity from these savages.

The Indians talked for a long time, but Lisha understood little Sioux. At last a tall Indian, evidently a petty chief, addressed him, "Where you go?"

"To the army camp," Lisha explained.

"White man paper say this Indian land. You stay out." He looked angry and spoke in a stern voice.

"The territory," Lisha said, "is forbidden to white settlers, to mining expeditions, and to wolvers, but I am none of these. I am on official business for the United States Army. I carry papers to Major Freeman."

"You lie!" the Indian said. "You no soldier."

Lisha understood that because he did not wear a uniform the Indians thought he could not be a soldier. He also felt sure that they knew about the army scouts and might even be acquainted with his fellow scout, Kelly. He also understood from the Indian's talk that the Indians had spotted him and Kelly at the big bend of the Yellowstone and had followed them past the mouth of the Shields River.

Lisha answered his accuser. "No, I am not a soldier. I am an army scout. Army chief say words on paper. I carry to other army chief."

The chief's face darkened. "White man's words on paper no good. Army chiefs no good. Indian here long time. White man army tell where Indian no can go. Kill all Indians same. Indian starve. He no care."

Lisha knew that the chief spoke the truth. He stood before the Indians, his head bowed in shame. For years the white men had disregarded the rights of the red men. They had broken their treaties. They had thought of the Indians as savages little better than animals, and now Lisha felt that he must pay part of the price for their folly. Other men had suffered for the wrongs of the whites against the Indians, but that didn't make his situation right now any easier to bear.

They led him from the council lodge and out of the village. A stout Indian with rope and stakes followed. He began to understand the fate they had prepared for him. He saw a large anthill just ahead. Stories flashed into his mind—stories of Indian torture that he had heard again and again on the Western plains.

Would they strip him naked? Would they stake him out here exposed to the blistering sun by day and the chill prairie wind by night while the ants drove him insane or he died of exposure? He'd heard that they had done such things. The Sioux! The terrible Sioux! He looked at the circle of dark faces and saw not one flicker of pity on any of them.

# 8
# PRISONER OF THE SIOUX

Lisha watched the Indians drive stout stakes into the ground on both sides of the big anthill. He saw them uncoil the rawhide thongs. He knew what the scene before him meant, but he seemed to be detached. The ropes, the stakes— They could mean but one thing and relate to but one person: himself. Yet he gazed as one in a dream.

Even when they stripped off his clothing, he made himself as one who does not care—who sees death spread before him and defies it. They tied his naked body over the anthill, all the time watching him and grunting to themselves in a satisfied way.

Lisha resolved that he would give them no cause for triumph. He knew well the Indians' respect for bravery, and his nature went along with the Indians. He would not cry out or moan or struggle. He would not beg for mercy or behave in any way different from the most heroic of their braves under similar circumstances.

As soon as his body touched the anthill, the ants swarmed over him. Their crawling and biting annoyed him, but the most pain came from his wounded shoulder. Would it get infected? His lips curled deliberately into a sardonic smile. The Indians, watching, grunted and looked at one another. Lisha faced reality. It couldn't matter whether his shoulder got infected or not. Nothing mattered anymore. He had never heard of any victim of the Sioux surviving this anthill torture.

When the heat of the day lessened and he knew that evening drew on, thirst began to plague him. He felt sure that he would not suffer long. The ants had now penetrated every body orifice and every square inch of his skin. Their stinging mandibles chewed with constant vigor. Lisha's thirst increased and became almost unbearable, yet it must be borne. He tried to move, but his least effort stimulated the hordes of ants to more intense activity. His mind reeled. He did not doubt that madness threatened.

The day faded, and darkness fell. The Indians left him, and he heard their footsteps and voices fade into the night. He looked up at the stars, brilliant in the sky, and he wondered about God. He had heard Elliot discuss the works of Ingersoll and Paine. He himself had been so much agitated over the doctrine of everlasting hellfire that he had determined never to worship a God cruel and unreasonable enough to torment human beings forever and ever. In spite of these things, he had never made up his mind about God. He had never got a Bible as he had promised himself that day when he drove away from the Bird Tail swing station.

The pain in his wounded shoulder and the ferocious ants kept him in constant torment. He looked at the moon and stars and recalled the Bible stories his mother had taught him, especially the one about the three Hebrew children in the fiery furnace. Could that story possibly be true? A strange thrill shook him. Suppose it had really happened. Would God be any different now from what He had been thousands of years ago?

Lisha faced the truth. No one but God could deliver him. He must fix his hope on the God who created the stars and the moon, who must have power to do anything. But what could he say to God? Why should God care about him, a man who had gone his own way, who had rebelled against God, who had not one good thing to recommend him?

The story of the prodigal son flashed into his mind. He decided that he would do just what that foolish and wicked young man had done: he would tell God the story of his life and ask Him for forgiveness. Racked with torment, tottering on the brink of madness, he recited his story and asked God for forgiveness and peace. Then he lapsed into unconsciousness.

Did he taste cool water? It seemed to him that someone held a dipper of water to his lips and that he drank. But he could not be sure. He knew only that he felt refreshed. Everything swam in a murky haze, and he saw the sun peeping over the horizon. Its first rays fell on his chilled body, and they felt good and comforting. Although he was still bound to the stakes and stretched across the anthill, a surprising thing had happened. The pain had gone from his shoulder. Even the ant bites didn't bother him.

He heard footsteps approach and knew that the Indians had come from the village. He knew that they expected to find a madman. He smiled at them as if enjoying a joke with them.

More Indians came. Lisha had not realized that so many Indians lived in that little cluster of lodges. Everyone in the camp must be there. Even the chief who had condemned Lisha to torture stood there looking down at his helpless prisoner.

Lisha wondered what they would do next. He had no more fear, only a deep peace.

The chief came over and began to untie Lisha's hands. He sat up at once and felt it a relief to straighten his back. He saw that some of the Indians objected to what the chief had done.

One old buck with a savage leer on his face picked up some dirt and rubbed it between his fingers and his thumb. "Dirt! Dirt!" he spat out the words with venomous spite. "You are nothing but dirt!"

Then he turned to the other Indians and spoke to them in the Sioux language. Lisha could not understand what he said, but the faces about him grew more menacing.

While they continued to argue, Lisha reached out and untied his feet. Then he sprang up and spoke in a loud voice. "You call me white dirt. You say white men kill all Indians. When did white man torture Indian as you have done to me? You are brave when you are many and I am only one and wounded." Lisha could see that the Indians listened. "Some of you have come to my village, and we have fed you and treated you kindly. I come here and you starve and torture me. Your hearts are not good."

The chief stepped between Lisha and the Indians. "No say more talk! Indian heart black today." He held out his hand. "You come."

The chief led him back to the village with all the other Indians following. In a lodge with a couple of guards, they gave him water and buffalo meat. Although the meat had not been salted, Lisha ate it with relish.

The sun beat down on the lodge, and it grew warm. Lisha felt so sleepy that he lay down on the floor. He wakened to find that darkness had fallen. Fresh water and food stood beside him. He ate again and refreshed himself with the cool water. Then he moved about the lodge to exercise his joints, still a little stiff from his exposure on the anthill.

Lisha talked with his guards in a friendly way about hunting and fishing. They could speak more English than he had supposed. They gave him a breechclout such as they wore.

The days went by, and the chief permitted Lisha to walk about the village, but he could not leave the circle of tepees. The Indian boys made constant sport of him when he appeared outside his lodge. They spat at him and threw dirt. To this behavior, Lisha paid no attention.

Before many weeks passed, the Indians moved their camp. On the first morning there, the chief came and told Lisha, "You go find wood with squaw. You no stay in camp lazy. You no try run away. We kill you!"

Lisha knew that nothing could be more insulting for an Indian buck than to be compelled to do squaws' work, but he welcomed the chance to get out of the stinking tepee and into the woodland or the prairie. Cottonwood, ash, and willow grew along the streams that fed the Yellowstone. On one of these streams they had set up their new camp. On the bluffs, dwarf pine and fir flourished. Lisha had always loved the open prairie and the woods. He worked hard gathering great bundles of wood.

The squaws approved of this arrangement. They could speak nothing but Sioux—had learned no English at all. They kept to themselves and spoke in their own tongue. Lisha found them a jolly lot of fat women who joked and laughed when the men were not around. They had a sense of humor and often played tricks on one another. They had their own particular wisdom of the woods and grasslands, which Lisha grew to respect.

One day as they worked, a little Indian girl screamed in sudden anguish. A rattlesnake had struck her leg. The squaws killed the snake and quickly gathered wild herbs, which they applied as a poultice to the snakebite. Lisha wondered what would happen. Should any white child suffer such a bite, she would be dead in a short time. The herb poultice seemed to work. The child quieted. Within a few days, the little one was playing as though nothing had happened.

Lisha thought back often to his night on the anthill and his prayer to God. He did not doubt that God had heard and delivered him. The matter of everlasting hellfire still puzzled him. He reasoned that if God is so tender and merciful to one poor man caught in the Indian torture, how could He possibly torment millions of men and women in hell? The whole nature of God had taken on a new meaning. He began to hope that he might find some way to escape and return to his family and friends at Bozeman.

Everything Lisha looked on had taken on a new significance. Nature became a revelation of God. He saw God's love in the infinite variety of His creation. He had made things good and beautiful for man.

Lisha began to learn the Sioux language. The squaws delighted to teach him new words. When he could carry on a broken conversation with them, they acted much pleased.

Once, just as the whole wood-gathering party started to return to camp,

Lisha sneaked into the brush, hoping that they would not see him—might not even miss him until morning. But the squaws had sharp eyes. They called him to come back, and with a heavy heart he went along.

One morning the bucks took Lisha along on a buffalo hunt. He rode along with the two dozen braves and felt glad. Maybe now he would be allowed to join in their hunts, but he soon found that they wanted him to do squaws' work again. He must skin the buffalo and cut up the meat.

Their hunt led them along the bank of the Musselshell River, and they discovered a small band of River Crows camped across the stream. Lisha knew that the Sioux and the Crow had been friendly for generations. Only since the white man's push west had crowded them had they had trouble. He wondered what they would do now.

The Crows mustered for battle with tremendous noise and activity. They plunged their horses into the river and swam across. Shooting and howling, they charged the Sioux at full gallop.

The Sioux wavered for a moment and then fled with the Crows in ferocious pursuit. They went only a short distance and then wheeled about and turned on their enemies. The Crows fled before them back to the river.

These wild charges and countercharges continued until the Sioux finally withdrew. Lisha estimated that perhaps a thousand shots had been exchanged. The only casualty—one dead horse!

More weeks passed, and Lisha failed to win the friendship of the Indians. Most of them never relinquished their hatred. Nevertheless, the Indians decided to adopt him into their tribe. None of the Indians had whiskers. They always plucked out the few hairs that grew on their faces. Now they held Lisha down while a squaw with a strong pair of tweezers pulled out all of his beard.

Although they had adopted him, they never fully trusted him. They did not leave him alone at night, but always bound his wrists and ankles. His skin became calloused, and the fetters did not annoy him anymore.

Lisha knew that in spite of their show of friendship, he could expect no safety among the Sioux. One day while he dressed a buffalo and strung the meat up to dry in the sun, a bullet whizzed by, barely missing his head. He knew that he must escape soon or be killed by the Indians.

# 9
# CHIEF LOOKING GLASS

Lisha had made one loyal friend in the Sioux village—a young Crow girl. While he worked with the squaws day after day gathering wood, he pitied the captive girl; and whenever he could, he eased the heavy burdens forced upon her. He often caught furtive looks that the Crow girl gave him and thought he detected sympathy in her lowered black eyes.

One night while his Indian guards slept and Lisha lay awake listening to their snoring and trying to plan some way to escape, he heard the slightest of sounds. Then he felt small hands on his wrists, then on his ankles. He realized that his midnight visitor could be none other than the captive Crow maiden. She had cut through the stout leather thongs that bound him. Now she took his hand, and he knew that she wished him to follow her.

Silent as two shadows, they crept outside the lodge. Then the girl released his hand, "Now you go," she said. "Someday you remember Crow girl."

He slipped through the darkness to the edge of the village. His heart beat so loudly with the excited joy of being free at last that he thought the sleeping Indians might hear it. If he could only get away from the lodges without discovery, he might have many hours head start of his pursuers. Certainly no one would find out until morning.

Just as he thought he had reached a safe distance, a snooping dog began to bark. Other dogs took up the alarm and joined in a crescendo of furious noise. Lisha still hoped that the village would not be aroused. The dogs often barked at night at each other, coyotes, and many times at nothing at all.

Then he heard voices and a commotion among the lodges. Men rushed about shouting that the thieving Crows were after the horses.

Lisha ran for the brush that lay along the water's edge. It seemed to him that every dog in the village had come awake to wild barking, and all of them ran hot on his heels.

He plunged into the water near the trunk of a giant cottonwood tree that had toppled into the creek. He saw wild parsnip growing at the edge of the stream and broke off a stalk. Then he climbed over the fallen tree trunk and crouched back under it as far as he could. If the Indians came too close, he could submerge and use his parsnip stalk for a breathing tube. This was a common trick among the Indians, and they would certainly spot him unless he held it close enough to the tree trunk so they could not discover it.

Then he heard the Indians approaching. He knew from what they said that they had seen his tracks at the water's edge and knew that he could not be far away. Ducking under the water, he worked himself farther back under the cottonwood log. He lay still as a stone and put the parsnip stalk in his mouth, being careful to hold it up among the branches.

Breathing through the stalk was not easy. He had to press his lips tight around the stalk and be careful not to wiggle it. An Indian waded out to the log and climbed over it. He almost stepped on Lisha, who compelled himself to absolute stillness. Finally, all sounds died away. The Indians must have gone on down the creek.

With deliberate caution, he pushed his head out of the water, straightened up, and looked in every direction. Nothing! No one! He swam across the creek and ran for the hills on the opposite side. Once in the hilly area, he raced to cover as much distance as possible before daybreak.

When morning came and daylight began to redden the sky, Lisha searched for a place to hide. He dared not travel or show himself by daylight. Even at night he might be discovered. He had lost his moccasins in the creek, and his feet hurt from the sharp rocks and the rough ground he had traveled over during the dark hours. He hid himself in a thick clump of sagebrush that stood waist high.

He could not keep strict count of the time but he knew that months had passed since the Indians had captured him. Autumn had come and the nights felt chilly. With no clothing but a buckskin breechclout, he huddled in the sagebrush and rested as much as he could until sundown.

When the next morning came, he looked down at himself. He felt his long matted hair. His skin had browned until he looked more Indian than white. Suppose he did manage to find his way back to the settlements; would anyone accept him? Would his own brother know him? And what chance did he have for survival? Spent with effort, hungry and thirsty, one man against the whole hostile Yellowstone country, how could he still hope?

Then he remembered how God had heard his prayer and delivered him from death on the anthill and healed his wounded shoulder. With new determination, he secluded himself in some shelter morning after freezing morning. By night he forced himself across the prairie, through washes and buffalo wallows. He ate wild fruit and drank at streams he crossed. Every day he hid and every night he traveled to the limit of his strength, always taking care that no skulking Indian discovered him!

At last he staggered into one of Nelson Story's cattle camps on the Yellowstone and knew that he had won his freedom. Yet he knew that without God's intervention, he could never have done it. Although sick from starvation and exposure, he still lived. Mitch Boyer, the intrepid Indian scout, came to look at him. He reached out and touched Lisha's tangled hair. "Man, you must have been through hell!"

The cowboys sent word to Elliot that his brother had escaped from the Indians. In no time at all, it seemed, Elliot, driving his horses at breakneck speed, swung into the cattle camp. "Oh, Lish! I thought you were dead!" His voice broke. Never had Lisha loved and valued his brother so much as at this moment of meeting.

Elliot had brought a comfortable wagon so that Lisha could ride home with as little jolting as possible. All the way back to Bozeman, he entertained Elliot with the account of his adventures in the Sioux camp. When he told him about how God had delivered him that night on the anthill, Elliot looked at him with a queer worried expression. Lisha could see that Elliot wondered if perhaps he was still a little mad from all he had suffered.

When the Rouse brothers rolled into Bozeman, almost the whole town turned out to welcome them. For the first time, Lisha realized how many friends he had and what good friends! He had left on his scouting assignment for the army in mid-June. Now October was half gone.

Under Elliot's loving care, Susan's kind attentions, and the tenderness of his sister Helen, Lisha's normally healthy body soon recovered, and his joy of life returned along with all his enthusiasm.

He had learned valuable lessons from his four-month ordeal. He now knew a great deal about the Sioux Indians, their language, customs, superstitions, and manners. But most important of all, he had met the living God that terrible night on the anthill, and he knew now that God had charge of people's lives and that He cared personally for Lisha Rouse.

Indians from most of the tribes in western Montana and northern Idaho visited Bozeman. The stores in the flourishing town offered all the things the Indians wanted, guns, powder, lead for ammunition. More and more Indians came to Bozeman to buy warm clothing for winter. They had learned to like flour, sugar, coffee, and other of the white men's foodstuffs. The merchants welcomed the Indian trade.

Clusters of lodges came to be a usual sight around the outskirts of town. Sometimes the Indians camped along the mouth of Bridger Creek north of town and sometimes on the east side of Bozeman. Whenever the townspeople saw a large band of Indians approaching, they sent Lisha out to discover their intentions. Were they interested in friendly trade or something else?

Some of the Indians became good friends of the businessmen in town. Others proved to be arrogant and demanding. One day an Indian came to the blacksmith shop where Billy Lee worked at shoeing a horse for Nelson Story. He demanded that Billy leave what he was doing and shoe his horse at once. Billy looked at him and said, "You must wait your turn with the others. Several men are ahead of you."

The Indian reached for his gun, but in a flash, Billy Lee drew his own weapon and shot the Indian dead. Lisha felt sure that the Indian could have known nothing about Billy Lee or he would never have laid hand on his gun. Billy enjoyed the reputation of the fastest gun in the territory.

One day a large number of Indians began to set up their lodges at the end of Main Street on Bozeman's east side. The scouts found out that these Nez Percé Indians had followed their chief, Looking Glass, on a journey from Idaho. They intended to camp near Bozeman to do some trading. Two hundred fifty lodges sprang up that evening, and the next day the Indians streamed into town to engage in some brisk trading.

Although the law forbade the sale of liquor to Indians, some of the young bucks got hold of firewater somewhere; and that night they made a great disturbance, fighting, yelling, and shooting off their guns. The noise alarmed the residents on the town's east side.

The following day a public meeting convened to discuss the disquieting events of the night before. Some of the men, alarmed and angry, made fiery speeches and demanded that the Indians be forced to leave the area at once. The merchants and others disagreed. Business had been slow and they needed the Indian trade. They urged some peaceful solution to the problem.

Some of the wiser among them began to question where the Indians had obtained the illegal liquor. No one seemed to know. Not one person would admit to having given an Indian whiskey or even having seen an Indian drinking whiskey.

They compromised at last by appointing a committee to take their grievance to Chief Looking Glass and to request him to keep his people out of town after dark. Those who had met the chief believed that he would cooperate and that the difficulty could be settled by peaceful negotiation.

Cooper, operator of the gun shop in Bozeman, led the delegation that sallied forth to the Indian camp. Cooper had met the chief, and he also had a good understanding of Indian ways and customs.

The chief came forward to meet his visitors and shook hands in cordial welcome. He called someone to come out and act as interpreter, and they conducted the three men into the camp. Here he showed them two splendid racehorses. Chief Looking Glass explained that he intended to race his horses against the best racing stock the Crows could offer.

He then showed them his war-horse, a beautiful white horse. He told them about other fine horses in his herd. Over an hour passed before the chief prepared himself to find out the white men's business.

He took them into his council lodge, ordered buffalo robes to be placed for them to sit on, and produced a peace pipe. The chief lighted it, took a puff or two, and passed it along until it had gone round the circle. Now the chief signaled that he wanted to hear what they had come to say.

Cooper explained in detail the drunken brawl of the previous night and how it had frightened the white families in the neighborhood. He drew out some knives and an old Navy revolver that had been picked up that morning on the ground where the fight had taken place. He concluded with a request that the chief would instruct his young men to stay out of the town after dark.

The old chief's face darkened, and a frown appeared. He looked sad. He sat in silence, and long moments passed before he spoke. The men looked at the chief's powerful frame. He had the body and bearing of an athlete, yet dignity and poise marked his every movement.

His moments of meditation ended, he began to speak soft and pleasant words. "Bozeman is the last place my people can buy sugar, flour, coffee, and clothing for the winter. We need powder and lead for our guns." He turned to Cooper. "We must have guns to defend ourselves from the Sioux and to kill game for food and for robes. The Indian needs the buffalo. The flesh is his food, and the skin keeps him warm in winter."

Now the chief's voice rose. "I am sorry that our young men disturbed your people. You are our friends. You say my young men behaved like fools. They may do foolish things when they are out of my sight. I cannot watch them every moment."

Chief Looking Glass shifted his position until he looked directly into the white faces before him. His black eyes flashed with piercing fire, and his voice took on a sharpness they had not heard before. "There is no firewater in my camp. We brought no firewater with us. I am told that the Big Chief at the city [the governor] has a book that talks. Book say white man must not give firewater to Indian, must not sell firewater to Indian."

He paused for a moment and looked at each of the three men separately. "You are our friends. I know you would not do this bad thing. But other men in this town do something different. They do not all sleep at same time. White men on your streets do not walk straight. They must have got firewater. Do all your people know of the Big Chief's book? If they know, why do they give firewater to my young men to make them fools?"

He sat back, his anger spent, his voice quieted. "My friends, you have wigwams where you live and work. You cannot see what all the people in your town are doing. You must have bad men who do not care about the words in the Big Chief's book. My young men brought no firewater to your town. Your people must have given it to them to make them fools."

He thrust out his hand in a gesture of command. "Go back to your town. Find those people who have forgotten the words of the Big Chief's book, and take the firewater away from them. I will see that my young men are fools no more and that you will be glad to see them when they come back in the spring and for many years to come."

A mask of sadness settled over the chief's noble features. "I have forbidden my young men to drink firewater, and my heart is dead when I find they have forgotten my words. Looking Glass has spoken."

The delegation from Bozeman rose and shook the chief's hand. They thanked him for his words of wise counsel and carried back the news that Chief Looking Glass would do his part in keeping peace and order.

Lisha thought that taking the firewater from the men who made a practice of giving it to the Indians would be difficult. However, Bozeman suffered no more from the rowdyism of drunken Indians.

58

# 10
# A SWEET LITTLE LADY

The closing of Bozeman Pass and the deactivation of the forts along the Bozeman Trail was a continual hardship on Bozeman. When the Indians successfully prevented the railway crews from surveying a line through the settlement, the town suffered another setback. But these discouragements only stiffened the settlers' determination. They resolved that the Gallatin Valley must be opened to white settlers along with eastern Montana.

Lisha, with other men who had a strong sense of justice, contended that the Indians had a right to their ancient hunting grounds. Lisha also felt that the continued wanton destruction of the buffalo was a significant injustice to the Indians. Anyone could see that the once vast herds of buffalo had diminished from their former numbers.

F. D. Pease, chief agitator for reopening Bozeman Pass and the Yellowstone, had no regard for Indian rights. "Lish," he said one day, "you're an Indian lover."

"I'm not," Lisha insisted, "but you've got to admit that Indians roamed the Yellowstone for hundreds of years before we were born. I want to see emigrant trains rolling west as much as you do, but settling the Yellowstone is just not possible now."

"Well, I'm in favor of building a fort to protect settlers," Pease went on. "We've got to drive an entering wedge into that Yellowstone country if we ever get anywhere. We've got to show those Sioux a thing or two."

"You'll bite off more than you can chew." Lisha stuck to his contention. "You'll have a constant fight on your hands, and you can't hold out unless the government backs you."

"Right!" Pease hadn't given up his idea. "We furnish the protection, and settlers will come. If we make the move, we'll get what we want."

But other matters absorbed Lisha's attention during those last months of 1875. Lisha had now passed his thirtieth birthday. For fifteen years he had lived the life of a Western frontiersman. He had freighted merchandise to the gold camps and flour from the mills in Bozeman to the army camps.

He had become friends with several different Indian tribes and learned their languages customs. They permitted him to drive his freight wagons through their territory without much difficulty. He even knew the Indian sign language.

During this summer, Lisha built a large log house in Bozeman. Elliot helped him. When they had completed the building, Elliot sold his house and moved into one part of Lisha's new home.

Lisha got on well with the miners and the white settlers in the Gallatin, but with the ladies he always felt shy and awkward. His friends often teased him about his bachelor state. He usually replied, "What woman would have a tough old bullwhacker like me?"

But this autumn a sweet little lady made a triumphal march right into Lisha's heart to reign as queen for the rest of his life. The day after Christmas of the year 1875, Lisha married Chastina Randall. As he looked down into the innocent face of his little bride and saw the trusting affection in her soft brown eyes, he resolved to make this lovely girl happy through all the years to come.

At the wedding reception, Lisha overheard some of the women talking. "Well, I'm glad," one woman said. "Now Chat will tame that wild, reckless daredevil."

"Maybe she'll teach him some religion too. Chat is a good Christian girl, you know," another lady joined in.

"I don't think Lisha is irreligious." The minister's wife defended him. "It's Elliot that's always arguing with my husband. Lisha is more like his sister Helen."

"Well, I think Lisha and Elliot are as like as two peas in a pod," the first woman insisted.

Lisha smiled to himself. These women did not know about that night on the anthill when, racked with suffering, he had looked up into the moonlit sky and had put religion to a test that had settled his belief in God for all time. They could not know that after his recovery from that ordeal, he had gone to his sister Helen and asked to borrow his mother's old Bible. He still had it.

With Helen's help, he had studied, and now he could never again doubt the existence of God as a personal Deity. Before his capture by the Sioux, he had often argued against belief in a God who would torment people in everlasting hellfire. Now, although the idea of hellfire still bothered him, he knew that God lived. God had heard his prayer and delivered him from certain death.

Lisha did not feel ashamed to pray, but he made no open confession of his faith. He felt it enough to have established a personal relationship with God in heaven.

Chastina and Lisha studied the Bible together. His young bride went to church regularly. It seemed to Lisha that she used every sweet artifice to persuade him to become a convert and attend church with her, but Lisha could not accept the belief that the soul is immortal. He read over and over a text in Ezekiel 18:4: "The soul that sinneth, it shall die."

To Lisha the text couldn't be plainer. Souls can die and do die. The more he thought about it, the more logical and reasonable it became that the souls of all men must die. He didn't even think the doctrine that good people went to heaven at death could be scriptural.

Some Sundays Lisha went with Chat to church, but he always seemed to choose a Sunday when the preacher spoke on some phase of the doctrine that the soul is immortal, or on hell, or everlasting punishment, or on the interest of loved ones "gone before" in those alive on the earth now.

Lisha rejected the thought that the dead could have knowledge of what living people did. One day he found the text in Ecclesiastes 9:5: "For the living know that they shall die: but the dead know not anything." Lisha read it over several times. He read it to Chat. "Now think about this verse, Chat; it says the good dead as well as the bad dead *know not anything*!"

"I can't argue with you." Chat gave him her sweetest smile. "Let's have a nice Sunday. I've cooked a good dinner."

But Lisha had to have one more word. "I've studied enough ancient history to believe that this doctrine of immortality of the soul came right out of paganism."

"It's always been one of the main points of my faith." Chat set the dinner on the table. "But I don't know enough to argue with you, and I can't explain it. Let's invite the preacher and his wife for dinner next Sunday."

"All right." Lisha sat up to the table. "That's the right thing to do."

Lisha liked to invite company. No other woman in town could cook a better meal than Chat, and he'd have a week to study deeper into this doctrine of the immortal soul.

The following Sunday when the minister and his wife came for dinner, Chat set out a delicious meal—a mound of white mashed potatoes with a pool of golden butter melted in the center, chicken and dumplings, rutabagas from Elliot's storage cellar fixed with rich cream, and hot rolls.

After they had eaten, while the women cleared up the dishes, Lisha and the minister sat in the front room and talked. Lisha opened the conversation. "Chat and I have been talking about hell and the eternal punishment of the wicked. Are there texts in the Bible that speak of punishment that will continue through all the years of eternity?"

"Yes, Lisha," the minister said, "there are several. Let us take Matthew 5:46: 'These shall go away into everlasting punishment: but the righteous into life eternal.' "

"Well," Lisha spoke in a thoughtful way, "don't you think that perhaps the 'everlasting' means everlasting in *effect,* not in *duration?*"

"No, Lish," he said. "Bring me your Bible. I'd like to show you some more texts." Lisha brought his mother's old Bible.

The preacher turned to Revelation 14:10, 11. " 'And he shall be tormented with fire and brimstone in the presence of the holy angels, and in the presence of the Lamb: and the smoke of their torment ascendeth up forever and ever: and they have no rest day nor night.'

"And," continued the preacher, "in Mark 9:43, we read of fire that shall never be quenched."

"Well—" Lisha leaned back in his comfortable chair. "I want to believe in God. I do believe in God, but I must believe that He is fair and just—at least as fair and just as a good man would be."

He leaned toward the minister. "Do you consider it fair and just to burn men in hell for millions of years, for the wickedness they do in a few years on earth? Only the most cruel tyrant could imagine such a thing!"

The minister cleared his throat. "No, Lisha, God is not a tyrant. He gives men every chance to accept Christ and be saved. But if man persists in doing wrong, he will be lost and must suffer the penalty of the damned."

"But look here!" Lisha jumped up and stood before the preacher. "When you take the texts you have just read by themselves, you could interpret them that way, but there are other texts that present a different angle. I think it only right to consider them too."

He picked up some sheets of paper on which he had written a number of texts that he had searched out with the help of the concordance in the back of the old Bible. The minister leaned forward in his chair. He appeared eager to hear what Lisha might have to present.

Lisha sat down again. "I think that any church doctrine which is not supported by *all* the scriptural teaching on the subject is in danger of misrepresenting God—placing Him in a false light."

The minister nodded.

Lisha reached for the Bible and read John 3:16: " 'For God so loved the world, that He gave His only-begotten Son, that whosoever believeth in Him should not perish, but have everlasting life.' What does *perish* mean?"

The minister smiled. "I see what you're getting at. *Perish* means to come to nothing, to be destroyed, to cease to exist."

"Doesn't *perish* describe the thing that will happen to the unrepentant— what believers will escape?" Lisha pressed his point.

"Go on, Lisha, I'm listening."

Lisha looked quickly over his list of texts: "The soul that sinneth, it shall *die*." Ezekiel 18:4. "The wicked shall be *cut off*." Psalm 37:28. "The wicked *shall not be*." Psalm 37:10. "A fire goeth before Him, and *burneth up* His enemies." Psalm 97:3. "And ye shall tread down the wicked; for they shall be ashes under the soles of your feet." Malachi 4:3.

"Oh, I have a lot more," Lisha said. "It isn't necessary to read them all, but they do add up to one pretty clear teaching—the wicked are going to come to nothing, to perish utterly. They are not going to be suffering in hellfire forever and ever."

"You've certainly spent a lot of time studying this subject." The preacher drew a deep breath and rose to go. His wife came in, and they put on their warm coats. "Would you let me borrow your list of texts, Lisha? I want to study them for myself. You've given me something to think about."

After they had left, Chat turned to Lisha. "I suppose they won't come back to our house anymore. The minister probably doesn't care to hear you expound your pet theories."

"Well, just because I don't accept his interpretation of the Bible on this point shouldn't affect our friendship. Didn't you hear him say that I'd given him something to think about?" Lisha slipped his arm around his little wife. "I think the preacher liked it."

"Let's hope you're right."

# 11

# THE RELIEF OF FORT PEASE

F. D. Pease had gone out and tried to establish a fort on the Yellowstone. But word came back to Bozeman that the fort had run into serious trouble. Dreams of a new opening for settlers had turned into a nightmare.

No settlers appeared, but swarms of Indians did. The military post which Pease had fondly hoped for never materialized. The Sioux declared unrelenting war on Fort Pease. Then the Sioux War broke out. Life at the fort became a series of skirmishes with hostile Indians, with the crack of the rifle the most familiar sound, augmented now and then by the boom of a cannon—an iron six-pounder which thundered over the valley. The men at the fort owed their present survival mostly to the cannon.

This incessant warfare imposed severe suffering on the small garrison. Although many an Indian bit the dust, six of the fort's defenders had died and nine others sustained serious injuries. When the garrison had been reduced to twenty-eight men, they appealed to Fort Ellis for relief.

General Terry took immediate action and dispatched Major Brisbin at the head of four companies of the Second Cavalry.

Lisha had been working for the army, and now General Terry made him wagon master of the supply train that must accompany Major Brisbin.

On Washington's birthday, 1876, Lisha bade his bride of two months goodbye and set off on another dangerous mission. Since Chat and he lived in a house which Elliot and Susan shared, he knew she would be well cared for and fully employed with Elliot's family.

Lisha had been over this trail many times when freighting goods from Bozeman. He knew every hillock, chuckhole, and ford. His knowledge proved fortunate indeed, for this February the trail lay under deep snow. When the caravan drew near the summit of Bozeman Pass, the wagon drivers found such deep snow that some of the wagons had to be helped over the pass by extra mules.

On descending to the Yellowstone country, they discovered the snow almost gone, and traveling became less difficult. But every mile they traveled exposed them to greater danger. The Indians of the whole area had risen in fury against the white settlers, and especially against Fort Pease.

As wagon master, Lisha rode his horse everywhere through the train watching for any trouble with the wagons. With constant attention, he managed to keep the supply train rolling along smoothly.

After three days of travel, the train camped at the remains of Fort Howie. Now Major Brisbin went on ahead to the Crow agency where he expected to pick up Crow scouts for the remainder of the trip to relieve Fort Pease. He promised to wait for the supply train at the agency.

Now Lisha must take his forty-two wagons over the Yellowstone, which measured about a hundred yards across at the ford. Although not deep, the current ran swift, and every team and wagon must be kept within the strict limits of the ford or they might get in water too deep for the animals to pull the wagons. Lisha worried about some of the horses, but by using dependable wheel teams, they managed to cross the ford without accident or much loss of time.

Lisha now received a message from Major Brisbin that he had finished his business at the Crow agency sooner than he expected and would now meet the supply train at a point lower on the Yellowstone.

When Lisha and his drivers overtook the cavalry, they found the camp almost empty. The officers and men had all gone fishing.

The wagon train made camp a short distance from the army tents. When the soldiers came back from their fishing trip, they brought enough fish to supply all four companies of cavalry as well as the men in the supply train.

The cavalrymen packed fresh supplies and left early the next morning. Lisha pushed on with his train as fast as he could, because he knew the urgency of the relief mission. The wagons would be needed to evacuate the wounded and carry supplies for the men.

Snow began to fall, and a north wind chilled the drivers. They got down from their wagons and walked along, swinging their arms and stamping their feet, but the wagons rolled on.

Before Major Brisbin reached Fort Pease, the Indians had retired. The relief expedition found the garrison worn with loss of sleep and wearied from constant battle. The survivors gladly accepted the opportunity to leave.

Lisha distributed the men among his wagons and saw that they experienced as little discomfort as possible on the homeward journey toward the Gallatin Valley.

One evening after the wagon train had made camp, a rider rode into the circle. Lisha recognized him as Mitch Boyer, the well-known Indian scout, guide, and cowboy, who had been at Nelson Story's cattle camp the day he had stumbled in nearly starved and more dead than alive after his escape from the Sioux.

Lisha welcomed Mitch, and the men sat around the campfire telling stories.

"Say, Lish." Mitch turned to him. "Have you seen Kelly?"

"No, I haven't seen or heard of him since the night the Sioux surprised us and took me prisoner."

"I saw him last fall," Mitch said. "He was fixin' to trap wolves this winter. He stopped at the agency for a couple of days. He asked about you."

"What did you tell him?"

"I told him you came into our camp starvin' and draggin' one leg." Mitch's eyes danced. "After he got through cussin' the Sioux, he said he'd sure like to see you."

Late that evening when everyone had quieted down for a few hours sleep, Lisha thought about Kelly. He felt glad that his fellow scout had survived that ordeal with the Indians.

At seven-thirty the following morning, Lisha had the supply train rolling, and a few more days brought the wagons to Bozeman Pass, where they descended into the Gallatin Valley and home.

Pease's effort, doomed though it had proved to be, did contribute to the overthrow of the Cheyenne and the Sioux Indians and the settlement of the Yellowstone. The Sioux War came on, and the Indians refused to return to their reservation even when ordered by the army to do so.

A short time after Lisha returned from his trip to Fort Pease, five companies of soldiers came marching through town on their way to Fort Ellis. They planned to join other soldiers at the fort, and together they would proceed to the Yellowstone to search out the defiant Sioux. General Custer would meet them on the Yellowstone with a company of soldiers from Fort Lincoln.

Excitement spread through the town. All the citizens of Bozeman rejoiced. Now surely the front door to Montana would open again, and the wheels of progress could roll forward once more.

All through the summer and fall of 1876, the news of the Sioux War disturbed Lisha. General Sheridan had sent three columns of soldiers under Generals Crook, Terry, and Gibbon to crush Sitting Bull and his Sioux warriors on the Yellowstone.

First came the report of General Crook's repulse before Crazy Horse. Then, shortly after, came the horrifying news of Custer's disaster. The Sioux, reinforced by Rain-in-the-face with a thousand Cheyenne warriors, had surrounded Custer's band and annihilated them. Custer had been outnumbered twenty to one.

General Reno, a subordinate officer who had attacked the upper camp of the Sioux, suffered a major defeat, and only prompt relief from General Terry and General Gibbon saved him and his men from destruction.

In the fall, word trickled back to Bozeman that Sitting Bull and about three thousand of his followers, after eluding the army all summer, had escaped into Canada.

Every citizen in Bozeman followed the news of the campaign with tremendous interest. Lisha often felt hemmed in and cooped up. His free spirit longed to be with General Terry's men over on the Yellowstone. He yearned for the wild plunge into danger.

In October of that year, Lisha and Chat welcomed their firstborn son, Charles Ernest. The advent of the new baby wrought a surprising change in Lisha that astonished all his friends. Now his interests became domestic and centered round his home and family. He knew that no finer boy than his Charley had ever been born in Montana or in the whole United States.

Two years later, Nelson Lee was born, and Lisha took a fresh look at his town, the place where his children would grow up. A fine class of settlers had been attracted to Bozeman, both in the farming and the business developments of the Gallatin Valley. He approved of what he saw.

Nelson Story, now a prosperous man with three cattle camps on the Yellowstone, owned and managed the Gallatin Valley National Bank. The State Agricultural College in Bozeman owed its establishment to a gift of land and several thousand dollars from Nelson Story.

Perry McAdow, one of the men whom Elliot and John Bozeman had persuaded to leave the wagon train and settle in the growing town, had now become an important citizen. His flour mill and other enterprises contributed much toward building the town's present prosperity. He became a member of the state legislature.

Both Lisha's and Elliot's families still lived in the big log house that Lisha had built the year he and Chat married; and now that Chat's younger sister, Lettie, had come to live with them, the little boys seemed certain to be spoiled by too much attention. It was at this time that Elliot began to build a new brick house.

Lisha's family of little ones brought much joy to Elliot's wife, Susan. She had no children of her own and took great delight in helping Chat with her work.

One day while Chat and Susan scrubbed clothes, Charley, then about three, came to them all excited and repeated words which they found difficulty understanding, "Ee in aole!"

They followed the excited child, and he led them to a place where a posthole had been dug. There they found Lee, Charley's little brother, head-first in the posthole. They pulled him out, brushed the dirt from his clothes, and rejoiced to find the baby unhurt. Then they understood what Charley had been trying to tell them: "Lee in a hole!"

Indians often traded in Bozeman, and among them came the "nontreaty" tribe of Nez Percé to buy rifles and ammunition. They had always been more or less friendly, but they refused to be bound by treaty to a reservation. Most of the white settlers thought well of them. Now the pressure of advancing white settlements began to affect even the Nez Percé and brought on increasing friction which threatened the peace.

A government commission appointed to hear the complaints of the Nez Percé decided against them and decreed that they must accept confinement to the Lapwai Reservation in Idaho Territory.

In May 1877, General Howard had orders to remove all "nontreaty" Indians to Lapwai Reservation. He gave the Indians thirty days to comply with government orders.

Some of the young warriors, resentful of government interference, murdered some white settlers near Mount Idaho. A military force sallied out to restore order, but suffered serious losses in combat with the Nez Percé tribe. Now the citizens of Bozeman saw the large quantity of firearms and ammunition they had supplied to the Nez Percé being used against the white settlers.

The rebellious Indians would not accept the reservation the government had allotted them. They insisted on possessing their ancient hunting grounds where they had killed buffalo for generations. Determined to have their own way, they decided to take flight from Idaho through Lolo Pass into the buffalo country of Montana.

Several hundred of them made their way into the Bitterroot Valley and on into Big Hole Prairie. At the foot of the Gibbons Pass, they camped near the north fork of the Big Hole River.

General Gibbon hastened to intercept them. On August 8, the scouts discovered the Nez Percé camp. The soldiers moved forward during the night and launched their attack at dawn. In the frightful melee that followed, women and children were slaughtered along with the warriors.

Lieutenant Bradley fell, fatally wounded. Within twenty minutes, the Nez Percé camp appeared to be in the hands of the attacking soldiers. But the Indians recovered from their surprise, rallied, and began firing from all directions at the soldiers, who retreated to a wooded point near the upper end of the camp. They took shelter behind fallen logs and trees and dug shallow trenches with their bayonets. Here they remained to fight for their lives.

The Nez Percé, however, had only been using delaying tactics while they could gather up their belongings and take flight toward their goal, the buffalo country. The United States Army continued the relentless pursuit until September 30, at Bear Paw Mountain, where Chief Joseph admitted defeat and said, "I will fight no more forever!"

Chief Looking Glass, that noble leader of the Nez Percé when they camped at Bozeman, died in the battle of Bear Paw Mountain.

The arrows that had pierced Custer's breast made Sitting Bull's doom certain. The names of Generals Crook, Gibbon, and Miles became household words in Montana. Now the defeat of Chief Joseph had subdued the Western tribes from Idaho Territory. The settlers began to feel and act like permanent citizens.

Thus peace came to Montana Territory. Now when Indians appeared in Bozeman, they came only on peaceful errands.

# 12
# HOMESTEAD AT FORT ELLIS

After the Indian wars of 1876 and 1877, quiet settled over the Gallatin Valley, and Bozeman continued to grow.

Lisha and Chat's family grew also. After Charles Ernest and Nelson Lee, three more boys were born to them: Claude, Oren, and Guy.

Little Oren lived for eighteen months only. Lisha and Chat knew their first deep sorrow when they stood at their baby's open grave. The preacher had spoken many comforting words. He told them that their child had now entered heaven and described how, even now, he played with other little angels among the fadeless flowers. Lisha realized that in his deepest thought, he had rejected the doctrine of the immortal soul. Little Oren couldn't be in heaven. He said nothing, because Chat seemed to take comfort from the thought.

Now occurred an event of major importance. The railroad came to Bozeman. The Northern Pacific, which had tried to bring the railroad into the valley ten years before and had been delayed by the opposition of the Sioux, now finished laying the rails, and the first train rolled into the town in August of 1883. Frederick Billings, the man for whom the city of Billings was named, and president of the Northern Pacific at that time, presided over the ceremonies.

Most of the town's citizens gathered on McAdow Hill to see the thrilling sight. Lisha's little family stood close to Elliot, who watched the whole scene with great pride. Many changes had taken place since he had helped Bozeman and Beall lay out the town. Lisha and Elliot looked into each other's faces and knew a shared moment of deep satisfaction. The brothers had

Heard the tread of pioneers
    Of nations yet to be;
The first low wash of waves
    Where rolls a human sea.
They crossed the prairies as of old
    The pilgrims crossed the sea

To make the West, as they the East,
    The homestead of the free.

"Now there will be a market for the coal from Chestnut," Elliot said, "and more lumber from the sawmills will go out to far places."

"Yes," Lisha added, "and Bozeman will become an outfitting point for travelers to Yellowstone National Park."

Lisha had a strong personal hope for the future too. He thought about it as he walked home with Chat and the boys. Now that the Indians had been subdued, he hoped that the government would abandon Fort Ellis. He felt that the soldiers were no longer of any help to the settlers. If they should be moved to some other place, he knew the citizens of Bozeman could manage well enough.

Lisha had lived with the Indians and knew their habits and customs. His words influenced many people. They circulated a petition that Fort Ellis be deactivated or moved.

One day Chat's sister, Lettie, took Lisha's two older boys downtown. She met Nelson Story's daughter, a friend and schoolmate, who asked the boys' names.

"The older one is Charles, and the younger one is Nelson Lee."

"Oh, is he named after my father?"

"Yes, I'm sure he is."

"Well, my father will be interested to hear about his namesake."

A few days later, Lisha came home and called Lee to him. "Mr. Story at the bank wants to see you, Lee."

"What for?"

"I suppose you've been into some mischief," Lisha teased him.

Lee went to the bank with reluctance, but he found the banker all smiles and friendliness. "You are Nelson Lee Rouse, aren't you?"

"Yes, sir."

"My name is Nelson too." Mr. Story held out his hand, and little Lee put his small hand into the big brown one. "I want you to do something for me. Will you carry this note to Mr. Wilson at the store?"

Lee carried the note to Wilson's General Store, and after Mr. Wilson read it, he supplied Lee with a complete outfit of new clothes and sent him home dancing with delight.

Some kind ladies invited Lisha's boys to attend Sunday School at the

Baptist church, and they kept going until the year 1889, when something happened to change everything for the Lisha Rouse family.

Fort Ellis had at last been deactivated. Now, after fifteen years, Lisha and the other settlers who had been dispossessed when the government established the fort moved back to their claims. A beautiful creek flowed through the land all the year round, and Lisha with Billy Lee had dug a ditch right across the place where Lisha had built his cabin. It provided water for domestic use, for stock, and for irrigation.

Billy Lee also returned to his former claim in a lovely spot just south of Lisha's place.

Lisha built an addition to his original log cabin and then erected a comfortable home (which still stands). His children numbered six when the family moved to the ranch. Pearl and Helen May had been added to the four boys. Here on the ranch the children enjoyed the free, active life that Lisha had always dreamed about as ideal for his family.

Four more girls were born during the early years on the ranch: Ruby, Elsie, Abby, and Sadie. Lisha and Chat delighted in their big family. The summer days were filled with work and fun, and winter brought its own kind of games and delights as well as work and study.

One day in October 1893, Lisha took Charley and Lee with him into the foothills to hunt deer. They came up over a ridge and surprised a lynx feeding on a dead horse. Before they could get a good shot, the lynx bounded into the bushes and vanished.

A day or two later, Lee came past the place on his way to return a borrowed gun to a neighbor. He climbed the ridge to see if the lynx might still be feeding on the carcass. He would be ready for him this time.

He crept up quietly and peered over the ridge. Yes, the lynx had come back to the dead horse. Lee raised his rifle and killed the animal with one shot. At the sharp report of the gun, several lynx bounded away. Lee aimed at another lynx and dropped it with a wounded shoulder. His third shot crippled another. It began crawling toward the brush dragging its hindquarters. Lee had only two bullets left. He ran to head off the lynx with the wounded shoulder. With a fierce growl it sprang at him, and he shot it through the head.

Now what should he do? He had one bullet left, and he must pass through a woods full of lynx. Perhaps he had come on a whole family of them. He must kill the other wounded lynx too.

Taking his knife from his pocket, he approached the animal, put his foot on its head, and cut its throat. Then he went on his way to deliver the borrowed rifle to the neighbors.

When he related his adventure to his parents that evening, Chat looked at Lisha. "Does he remind you of someone?"

Lisha thought back to his own adventures when he and Elliot had first come to Montana. "He's beginning a little early at fourteen; but, yes, I'd say the boy comes naturally by his love of danger."

West of Lisha's farm lay the Reynolds homestead. Lisha observed his neighbor and thought him a strange person. He seemed to be a first-rate farmer, but he had queer religious ideas. A preacher came to Bozeman and pitched a big tent on a vacant lot. And this man Reynolds helped him—an odd thing indeed. Of course, Lisha never went near the big tent, although preaching services continued for several weeks.

After Lisha finished building his ranch house, he began to invite the neighbors for dances. He liked having gay people around him, and both Chat and he enjoyed dancing.

The Reynolds family never came to the parties, although Lisha always invited them. They visited in the most friendly manner at other times, exchanging work and neighborly visits.

One day as Lisha started to cross the pasture to invite the Reynoldses to a dance, Chat said, "Those people don't think it's right to dance, Lisha. I just found out. It's against their religion."

Lisha turned back. "Well, then, we won't ask them anymore. I respect any man's conscience."

Fall came, and the threshing rig with its crew of farmers made the usual round of the wheat farms. The man who owned the rig in the Fort Ellis vicinity came by one evening, and Lisha could see that something had excited him.

"I've just come from the Reynolds place," the man explained. "I went to tell Reynolds that we'd be at his place Saturday morning." He slid down from his horse, walked over to Lisha, and took hold of his shoulder. "He wouldn't have it! He wouldn't have it, Lish!"

Lisha knew, everyone in the neighborhood knew, that the Reynoldses kept Saturday for Sunday, but anything so important as threshing— Why, their winter food depended on it. The crop in the area had been heavy, and now the snow would soon fly. The man must be crazy. "I suppose you can't get back to him until the other farmers are taken care of."

"No, and that's exactly what I told him." The man spat a wad of tobacco on the ground. "D'you know what he said? 'Even if I lose my whole crop of wheat, I will not violate God's holy Sabbath!' "

Lisha looked over to the west where he could see the Reynolds farm lying golden in the autumn sun, the fields covered with shocked and stacked wheat. "He's got a big crop—best he's ever had, I think."

"That's just it," the thresher said. "I never saw anyone so stubborn. Can't he think of his family? They'll suffer if the snow falls before I get back to his job."

After his visitor rode away, Lisha stood thinking. None of the farmers in the valley would think of refusing to have their threshing done on Sunday, if their turn came on that day. Why did Reynolds think his Sabbath so special? Lisha puzzled about the question while he went about his chores.

Before the threshers could return, snow fell and more snow. The neighborhood lamented the foolishness that had caused Reynolds to leave his whole wheat crop out in the open field rather than have it threshed on Saturday.

Finally, late in the fall, the threshers came back to the Reynolds farm. Lisha drove one of the bobsleds that hauled the grain out of the field to the threshing machine. Amazed, he and the other neighbors saw that the wheat had suffered no damage and ran almost fifty bushels to the acre. Lisha watched the steady flow of perfect golden kernels stream from the separator's spout and felt a strange sensation. Had God really protected the man's crop?

After this experience, Lisha often visited his neighbor, and the talk usually ran to religion. Lisha told him of his capture by the Sioux and how God had answered his prayer for healing and deliverance. "Do you think it strange that God should answer the prayer of a sinner like me?"

"No, Lisha, I don't think it strange at all," Reynolds replied. "God answered Jonah's prayer even when Jonah was running away from Him."

"Well, then, tell me something." Lisha sat down on a stump and prepared for a long visit. "If God answers the prayers of sinners when they're still alive, why does He burn them in hell forever and ever after they're dead?"

Neighbor Reynolds sat down on a wagon tongue. "I don't believe the Bible teaches that God does any such thing."

Lisha felt a shock of surprise. All the Christian people he knew believed in everlasting hellfire. And the better Christians they were, the more they believed it and the more they talked about it. He felt a distinct letdown. "Don't you believe there's a heaven to win and a hell to shun?"

"Yes, I do." Reynolds leaned forward and fixed his eyes on Lisha. "I believe there's a heaven to win and a hell to shun, but I don't believe that sinners are being tortured in hell now or that they will be tortured forever and ever." Reynolds got up from the wagon tongue, came over, and laid his hand on Lisha's shoulder. "The results of their sin will be fixed forever and can never be changed. The *duration* of their punishment is another thing. God is just. He will not allow any man to suffer beyond what is just and merciful."

Lisha spoke up. "Doesn't the Bible say somewhere that the wicked will be punished with unquenchable fire?"

Reynolds stood with his hand still resting on Lisha's shoulder. He didn't say anything for a long time, and Lisha felt sure he'd stumped the man with his last question. He felt even more sure when his neighbor said, "Tell you what, Lish, you should get out your Bible and find all the texts on this subject. I'll do the same, and then we'll get together and compare our findings."

"Sounds like a good idea to me." Lisha walked home remembering how he had hunted out all those texts for the Bozeman preacher years before. Could he find that old list? Then he remembered that the preacher had never returned it. He'd have to make up a new list. How many years had that been? Just a few weeks after he and Chat married, they had asked that preacher to Sunday dinner. Now their older children were teenagers. Lisha ran a livery stable in Bozeman, and Elliot found him one day in his little office with a Bible open before him. He had written almost a full page of notes and texts.

"Who do you plan to stump this time, Lish?"

Lisha looked up at his brother. "Maybe this fellow will stump me. He's different." Lisha knew Elliot's infidel beliefs, and he chose his words with care. "This fellow, my neighbor, Reynolds, doesn't believe that people have immortal souls. He doesn't believe anyone is being tormented in hell now. He doesn't believe that anyone is going to suffer in hell forever and ever."

"You don't say!" Elliot sat down on a bench.

"He believes that God will deal with a man according to what he has coming—will reward him according to his works."

# 13
## A LOT OF QUESTIONS

For some unaccountable reason, Elliot seemed willing to discuss religion. He agreed with Lisha that it would be more reasonable to believe that God will deal with a man according to the way he has lived. "But it doesn't agree with the book *Sabbath Readings* that our father used to read to us. You were too little to remember, but I do. It described a broad, deep valley with a countless multitude of lost souls suffering flaming torment. An enormous high bridge spanned the valley, and on the Sabbath day the saints could walk out on the bridge and view the tormented souls, could 'feast their eyes' on the sight, the book said."

"I don't remember that book," Lisha said, "but I've heard preachers right here in Bozeman say practically the same thing and they said they got it out of the Bible."

Elliot stood up and faced Lisha. "Can you conceive of any ordinary decent man like you or me having a sense of justice that offers more mercy than the God of this Bible?"

"No, I can't," Lisha said, "but this fellow Reynolds claims the Bible doesn't teach any such thing."

"Well it does, and you know it, Lish!"

Lisha pointed to the paper he had written on. "After looking up these texts, I'm half inclined to think Reynolds may be right."

Elliot jabbed his finger toward the Bible. "It won't do you a bit of good. That Bible is just a bunch of visions and folk tales of the Hebrew people."

Elliot spoke with such emphasis and gestured with such fervor that Lisha thought best to switch the conversation to other topics. He didn't agree with his brother, but he had learned long ago that nothing could be gained through argument.

Before Lisha completed his list of texts for neighbor Reynolds, startling news hit the Fort Ellis community. A minister of the Seventh-day Adventist Church had made arrangements to hold a series of meetings in the Fort Ellis schoolhouse. Lisha knew that the Reynoldses belonged to that church.

The preacher, a man named Martin, came; and the meetings opened.

Lisha and his family attended every night. After the service, Lisha always went home, got out his Bible, and compared all the texts the minister had used with the same ones in his own Bible. He discussed the different sermon topics with Chat. He saw that she seemed to be much taken with this new religion.

One day Chat said, "Lisha, what do you think; should we invite this preacher, Martin, to dinner?"

"I don't see why we shouldn't. He's staying over at the Reynoldses. No need for them to have to feed him all the time." Lisha hesitated. "Anyway, there are a lot of questions I want to ask him."

Chat laughed. "Like, how can a loving God torment people in ever-lasting hell?"

"Yes, I do want to ask him that," Lisha admitted, "and I've just thought of another question. If the good are all in heaven and the bad are all in hell, then why does Christ need to come the second time? Remember what he preached last night?"

Lisha picked up the Bible where he had marked a text. He read the words: " 'For the Lord Himself shall descend from heaven with a shout, with the voice of the Archangel, and with the trump of God: and the dead in Christ shall rise first: then we which are alive and remain shall be caught up together with them in the clouds, to meet the Lord in the air: and so shall we ever be with the Lord.' " He closed the book with a feeling of triumph.

"Where did you read that from?"

"First Thessalonians 4:16, 17."

"Well, maybe we'd better not ask the minister to dinner if you are going to start a fuss."

"Oh, Chat, I won't start a fuss. I just want to know what he will say." Lisha really wanted to know the truth.

So the minister came and enjoyed one of Chat's excellent meals. Afterward, when they settled down in the parlor, Lisha began his questions. "Why did a good and loving God create a devil?"

"I don't believe that God ever created a devil," Pastor Martin replied. "I think the devil is self-made." He drew a Bible from his satchel and read: " 'Thou wast perfect in thy ways from the day that thou wast created, till iniquity was found in thee.' "

Lisha leaned forward in his eagerness. "Where are you reading from?"

"Ezekiel 28:15," the pastor said. "You might read Isaiah 14:12–14 too. It tells us that Lucifer became so proud and lifted up that he tried to take God's place."

Lisha turned to the texts in his Bible and studied them for several minutes. "Yes, they make the matter clear. But doesn't it seem to you that God and the devil are really working together in the punishment of the wicked?"

"Why, no, I can't see that," Martin said. "I can't see that they are working together at all. The devil is God's enemy."

"So I've been told." Lisha got into his subject. "But if that's so, how can a just and loving God turn wicked people over to the devil to punish throughout all eternity?"

"I'm afraid, my friend, that you are confusing the teaching of the Bible with a pagan belief adopted into the Christian church without any scriptural support," Pastor Martin said. "The Bible teaches that the devil and his angels will be burned up. There will be neither 'root nor branch' remaining. Read Malachi 4:1 and Revelation 20:12–15. The wicked people will be destroyed with them. So, you see, there couldn't possibly be any devil with a pitchfork to torture them through eternity."

"Doesn't the Bible say they will be tormented day and night forever and ever?"

"Yes, it does, but how long is *forever*?"

"I've always supposed it meant for all the years of eternity," Lisha said. "Is there any other meaning?"

"The punishment is forever in *effect*, not in *duration*. The Bible says the wicked will be reduced to ashes. Read Malachi 4:3. Do you remember the story of Sodom and Gomorrah?"

"Yes," Lisha said, "fire fell on Sodom, and only Lot and his two daughters escaped. The Dead Sea covers the spot where those cities once stood."

"Correct. Now look at this text." The preacher opened his Bible to the book of Jude and pointed to the seventh verse. "Read it aloud."

Lisha found the verse and read: " 'Even as Sodom and Gomorrah, and the cities about them in like manner, giving themselves over to fornication, and going after strange flesh, are set forth for an example, suffering the vengeance of eternal fire.' "

Lisha looked at the text a long time. An example, an *example* it said, of "eternal fire." But Lisha remembered that the Sodom and Gomorrah fire had raged until it reduced those cities to ashes. "Well, well," he said, "for the first time in my life I see through this thing."

Then he explained to Pastor Martin how confusion about the condition of the dead and the punishment of the wicked had troubled him since his youth.

The preacher said something that stirred a memory in Lisha's mind. "You see, friend Rouse, the only fair way to study the Bible is to take all the texts about a certain subject and consider them together."

Lisha had said the same thing to the Bozeman preacher on that Sunday so many years before. Today he had come another step along the road to truth.

The meetings continued in the schoolhouse, and after every sermon the Rouse family discussed the subject at home. Charley and Nelson Lee, Lisha's two older sons, declared that the preacher "seems to be teaching the truth."

"If they weren't Advents," Lee said, "I'd join that church."

One evening the minister announced his subject as "The Sabbath." Lisha sat forward in his seat, notebook in hand. He mustn't miss a single point. He'd wondered for a long time why everyone kept Sunday for the Sabbath. Also neighbor Reynolds's experience with the threshing crew still stood clear in his mind. Remarkable how that wheat had kept so well under the snow. He could still see in memory the stream of golden kernels and the astonished looks on the neighbor men's faces. He remembered that Reynolds hadn't seemed surprised at all, as though he had expected the wheat to be protected. Queer thing!

The minister traced the history of the Sabbath from Creation in the book of Genesis through to the last book of the Bible, Revelation. He invited anyone in the audience who could point to a text that authorized Sunday keeping to come forward.

Lisha looked around and saw that his neighbors and friends all seemed firmly settled in their seats. None of them made any move to stand up or go forward or anything. Did they all think that God meant for everyone to keep the seventh day? Or perhaps they knew of some text yet felt timid to stand up. Lisha knew there must be such a text, but he couldn't recall the words.

The Rouse family hurried home and began looking through their Bibles, using the concordance to assist their search.

"I'm sure there's a text here somewhere. I've heard the preacher read it," Chat said.

Lisha felt sure there must be more than one text commanding Sunday observance, else why did almost all Christian people regard it as a sacred day? But even with the aid of the concordance, none of the family could find even one text.

Before the next meeting in the schoolhouse, the circuit rider came to call on the Rouse family. They always looked forward to his visits. This time Lisha welcomed him with special enthusiasm. The minister had barely taken off his overcoat and hat when Lisha questioned him, "Why do you keep Sunday as the Sabbath?"

The preacher did not hesitate, "Haven't you read Hebrews 10:25 where it says, 'Forsake not the assembling of yourselves together upon the first day of the week as the manner of some is, and so much more as ye see the day approaching'?"

"There!" Chat said in a relieved voice. "I knew I'd heard that text somewhere."

Lisha could not answer. The circuit rider had stumped him for sure. He turned the conversation to other matters, but when the visit ended and the door closed on the visiting clergyman, he grabbed his Bible.

A moment later, he stormed into the kitchen holding the open Bible in his hand. He pointed to the text in Hebrews and read in a loud voice, " 'Not forsaking the assembling of ourselves together, as the manner of some is; but exhorting one another: and so much the more, as ye see the day approaching.' Listen to that, Chat; it doesn't say a thing about the first day of the week!" He raised his voice still higher. "That old hypocrite!"

Then he heard the preacher stomping into his overshoes on the back porch. "I thought he had gone," Lisha whispered. "Do you suppose he heard what I said?"

"Don't see how he could help it." Chat looked up and smiled. "I'm sure the circuit rider won't be back to our place."

The next day Pastor Martin came to call, and Chat did not wait for him to take off his overcoat. "Please tell us why all the churches keep Sunday. If there is no command in the Scripture, where do they get the authority to do it?"

Pastor Martin took off his coat and settled himself before the fire before he answered. "Mrs. Rouse, you remember that soon after the apostles died a great apostasy came in. Paul foretold it, said it had already begun to work in his time. During that apostasy many pagan beliefs and practices came into the church." He took out his Bible.

"Do you mean to tell us that the Bible doesn't say anything at all about a change?"

"Oh, yes, the Bible speaks of a change, but not the kind of change you're thinking of," the pastor explained. "It speaks of an apostate power which would 'think to change times and laws.' Look up Daniel 7:25."

Lisha spoke up. "Pastor Martin, didn't the apostle Paul preach on Sunday? Seems to me I've read such a text."

"The text you refer to is Acts 20:7. It doesn't use the word *Sunday*. In New Testament times, Sunday was called the first day of the week." The pastor turned to the text, and so did Lisha. The pastor read the verse: " 'Upon the first day of the week, when the disciples came together to break bread, Paul preached unto them, ready to depart on the morrow; and continued his speech until midnight.' "

"There! That's the text I've been looking for," Chat said. "It seems plain that they conducted their worship on Sunday and celebrated the Lord's Supper."

Pastor Martin smiled. "If breaking bread made the first day holy, then all the days of the week are holy. Turn to Acts 2:46." He flipped the pages of his Bible to the text. " 'They continued daily with one accord in the temple, and breaking bread from house to house.' "

"I see." Chat spoke in a much lower tone. Lisha could see that the last point had impressed her deeply. He felt impressed himself. Neighbor Reynolds could be right about this Sabbath business.

"Just one more thought." Pastor Martin opened his Bible again. "The Sabbath commandment is in the heart of God's law. And listen to what Jesus said about that law: 'Think not that I am come to destroy the law, or the prophets: I am not come to destroy, but to fulfill. For verily I say unto you, Till heaven and earth pass, one jot or one tittle shall in no wise pass from the law, till all be fulfilled. Whosoever therefore shall break one of these least commandments, and shall teach men so, he shall be called the least in the kingdom of heaven: but whosoever shall do and teach them, the same shall be called great in the kingdom of heaven.' Matthew 5:17–19."

The preacher explained that jots and tittles were tiny marks something like our dot on an *i* or the cross on a *t*. "The Ten Commandments contain fifty-five jots and thirty-five tittles. Our Savior says not one shall pass away until all be fulfilled."

Chat had to admit that Jesus could hardly have changed the Sabbath—not with those strong opinions He held about the unchangeable nature of the Ten Commandments.

From that day, Lisha could see a change in Chat. He knew that she had become more and more convinced that neighbor Reynolds and his wife had the real truth. Next thing she would be wanting to join their church. He felt sure of it.

# 14
# AT EVENING TIME—LIGHT

One morning Lisha woke up so discouraged that after breakfast and chores, he went to the bedroom and lay down on the bed. He wondered how he could manage with all his problems. He had borrowed money to enlarge his livery stable. Now the note would come due in a few days, and he didn't have the money.

Chat came in and found him. She looked him over with a worried expression on her face. "What's the matter, Lisha, are you sick?"

"Everything's gone wrong," he said. "Money problems—big ones. And on top of all that, you want to join the Adventist Church."

For a moment Chat did not speak. Lisha tried to read her thoughts. She looked so serious and yet so calm. "Maybe I shouldn't join the church."

With a rush of tenderness, Lisha remembered that Chat had never opposed him, had always done what he wanted. He threw his arms around her. "Chat, don't ever let anyone stand between you and your convictions—not me or anyone else!"

The meetings came to a close. Lisha went willingly to witness the baptism in the creek by old Fort Ellis. Chat and three of his children, Pearl, Claude, and Ruby, followed their Lord's example and received baptism that day.

Lisha watched Chat's face as she rose from the water and thought he had never seen it so beautiful. Mrs. Reynolds met her at the water's edge and embraced her with tender kisses and weeping. Lisha led his family away to the warm clothes he had ready for them.

In the days that followed, Lisha thought about baptism. Somehow he felt that he had made his discovery of God and had accepted Him on that anthill in the Sioux camp so long ago. He had never doubted God since that night. He surely didn't need any church to bind him to God. The cords were already strong and true.

Now it seemed to Lisha that everything moved faster. The children grew so rapidly. Charley went away from home to work, and Lee went into

Bozeman to stay with Uncle Elliot and Aunt Susan and attend high school there.

Elliot still held to his infidel beliefs and often talked to Lee about them. The boy's science studies at high school together with Uncle Elliot's persuasion influenced Lee. Lisha and Chat could both see it.

One weekend when Lee came home, he tried to show his mother why she must be mistaken about her new religion. "Mama, how old is the earth?"

"About six thousand years since God fitted it up for man at Creation." She studied his face. "Why do you ask?"

"Well, you see, science has proved that it is much older." Lee gathered enthusiasm as he talked. "Actually, the Bible has been discovered to be only a collection of myths and folklore."

Chat sat down stunned, not because she had no answer for Lee's argument, but because her precious son had already embraced his uncle Elliot's infidel beliefs.

Lee stood looking at her. Did he mistake her shocked silence for confusion? "Just give me one of those Advent books of yours," he said. "I'll study it, and I'll come back and tell you how wrong they are."

Without answering any of his arguments, Chat stepped to the bookcase and selected *Thoughts on Daniel and the Revelation,* by Uriah Smith. She handed it to him. "Now, Lee, if you can honestly think, after reading this book, that the Bible is only folklore, I will have nothing further to say. But be sure to return the book soon. Your father has been studying it, and he will want it back."

"Thank you, Mother." Lee made ready to depart. "I will bring it back in a week or so."

Days passed, weeks, a month. Then one day Chat stopped Lee. "When are you going to bring my book back?"

"Do I have to bring it back so soon, Mother?" He smiled down at her. "I find it most interesting. I'd like to keep it a while longer."

More weeks passed. What could Lee be doing with that book? Lisha and Chat asked that question often.

Then one Friday Lee came home with the book. He handed it to his mother and said, "Mama, I'm ready to join your church!"

Chat could not speak from astonishment and joy. She threw her arms about her son and wept for gladness.

Then Lee explained that he had studied the prophecies of Daniel and the Revelation and could see that God must indeed have shown the prophets, Daniel and John, the history of the future events that would happen hundreds and thousands of years from their time. Only God could have such foreknowledge. So another of Lisha's children accepted God's truth and joined the church.

In 1904, Adventist believers in the Gallatin numbered only a few. Five families lived in Cottonwood Canyon, twenty miles south of Bozeman. Several families lived in Bozeman, and Lisha and his family lived at Fort Ellis. The Reynolds family had moved away.

All these people felt a deep concern for their children. Should they not be educated in a church school? They talked it over and decided to rent a house in Bozeman and employ a teacher.

They built a little church, and the following year they moved the school to the church building and enlarged it to include ten grades. Twenty-eight children attended school that year.

More and more, Lisha found his thinking and his planning shaped by the faith that his family had embraced. He began to extend his vision of the future beyond this life to the hope of the everlasting life. He understood it now. Jesus would confer immortality on His people at His second coming.

On the night of the first school program, Lisha and Chat sat together in the audience. Lisha looked around the room and liked what he saw. The students seemed bright and happy. They even acted friendly toward their teachers.

His mind went back to his own brief school days. The schoolmaster usually wore out several willow switches every day. The students expected to be cuffed and slapped, or at least rapped across the knuckles with a ruler. All his youthful companions had considered the teacher an enemy to be endured or dealt with according to the weapons they possessed.

Now he watched members of the little school orchestra take their places. He listened with surprise and pleasure to the opening number. Lisha glanced around at the audience and saw his own pride and delight mirrored on every face.

He sensed that this church school managed children and educated them in a different way from what he had experienced. On the way home, he told Chat that the school had convinced him of the value of Christian education.

Lisha often pondered on the strange way he had been led among the many dangers and temptations of his pioneer life. Now, bound up closely in a family and a community of people who talked temperance and lived by Christian ideals, he saw his children growing up with the influence of the church and the church school strong upon them.

Never among all the thrilling adventures and the wild excitement of the gold camps had he felt so much satisfaction. No period of his life had been so blessed.

By 1906, the school had grown too large to be accommodated longer in the church building, and the men of the church decided to find larger quarters—land where they could build a permanent school with dormitories for boarding students who lived too far away to drive back and forth every day. They wanted a place in the country where the students could work on a farm and where industries could be developed to assist the students financially as well as to furnish training in useful skills.

Lisha offered them twenty acres of land at half its value, and they accepted his offer. So Mount Ellis Academy came into being on the very land where Lisha had taken up his squatters claim when Bozeman itself was but a dream of brave pioneers.

"Swifter than a weaver's shuttle" the years fled away. Bozeman had come into good and prosperous times and fulfilled all the expectations that Elliot, John Bozeman, and William Beall had cherished in the days when Indians roamed the wilderness and the land lay in virgin solitude.

Elliot's good and generous wife, Susan, passed to her rest. Now Elliot, grown old and lonely, lived by himself in his big brick house. His children had gone to homes of their own. He comforted himself by roving through the streets of Bozeman marking all the growth and the many surprising developments that took place every year. He seemed to take personal pleasure in the town's prosperity. With pride, he looked on the towering grain elevators and the humming flour mills. The mention of how he and John Bozeman had persuaded McAdow and Cover to invest in the mills always brought a smile to his lined face, which still retained its early fierceness. The McAdow-Cover Mill had been the first commercial mill in Montana.

The curtain was lowering on the pioneer days in Bozeman. The old actors had passed off the stage. Elliot often walked past their graves in the cemetery, and he knew that he would soon find his place there too. He decided to sell his home in town and spend the remaining years of his life with Lisha and his family at Fort Ellis.

The tie between the brothers had always been strong, and never was it more so than now when Elliot, old, bitter, and lonely, came for comfort to Lisha's home.

The townspeople had always spoken of the strong resemblance between the Rouse brothers. Now they seemed not at all alike. Elliot smoked constantly on his old pipe and drank to excess. These habits, together with his cynical unbelief, made him irritable and cranky. Lisha presented a marked contrast. Firmly situated in the heart of a genuine Christian family with gentle Chat and her sweet influence always drawing him toward good and better things, with his large family being educated in a Christian school and trained for Christian service, Lisha now enjoyed the golden time of his life.

Although not a church member, he took great pride in his children's development and all their plans. He neither smoked nor drank, and he taught his boys the evils of tobacco and liquor. He enjoyed frolicking with his children and taking part in their fun.

One hot afternoon in July, Elliot's life ended. He had been helping Lisha's boys prepare irrigation ditches when he suddenly collapsed from a heart attack. Loving hands laid him to rest beside Susan in Sunset Hill Cemetery where John Bozeman had been buried so many years before. Elliot had come back to rest at last on land that had once been part of his squatter's claim.

Time had left its mark on Lisha and Chat. Now a new generation of youngsters called them Grandpa and Grandma. Like the land whose rugged features civilization had softened, their faces had altered with the years, and their voices had softened and gentled.

From the time that Chat had joined the church, she had conducted family worship. Every day the family gathered, and always in their prayers they pleaded for "Papa" to join them in open acknowledgment of his faith in God and all the church stood for. Yet they attended church and prayer meeting without him.

"I can't bear to think of your father being taken by a heart attack like Uncle Elliot," Chat said to Pearl one day. "It is important to his soul's salvation that he give himself to God openly and join the church."

"I can't understand it," Pearl said. "He seemed the most enthusiastic of us all when he first heard the truth. Remember how convinced he was about the Sabbath?"

Early one Sunday evening in 1915, two of Lisha's young people, Claude and Ruby, prepared to drive into Bozeman to attend a meeting. R. D. Quinn, a family friend, would speak that evening.

"Why don't you come with us, Papa? Wouldn't you like to hear Elder Quinn?" Ruby had already climbed into the buggy.

"Elder Quinn? Well, yes, I would like to hear him; but I'm afraid I'll make you late."

"We'll wait for you," Claude assured him.

Lisha could see that the family seemed amazed that he would go along to church. He didn't quite know, himself, why he wanted to go tonight.

He got ready, came out, and climbed into the buggy with Claude and Ruby. They drove into Bozeman. Lisha felt that Elder Quinn must have prepared the sermon with him in mind. He felt the drawing power of the Holy Spirit work with mighty effect on his heart and mind. A presence he could not explain stirred the deepest level of his soul.

Elder Quinn closed his sermon with an appeal to all who accepted Christ as their personal Savior to come forward.

Lisha rose and went forward to the altar, and a peace he had never before imagined filled his being. At the close of the meetings, he was baptized. Chat and the children rejoiced as only those who have waited long years can rejoice.

Now on Sabbath mornings, the white-haired patriarch led his family across the road from his house to the chapel at Mount Ellis Academy, where services were conducted.

For years Lisha had lived and worked and survived in a wild and lawless land ruled by the gun and the knife. For many years he had scouted for the army and taken part in battles with the Indians. For eleven years he had been a policeman in Bozeman and carried a gun everywhere he went. Many times in his life he had used the six-gun and the rifle with deadly effect.

Now, instead of a gun, an open Bible lay on his lap as he followed the preacher's texts with grave interest. Sometimes he caught Chat's affectionate eyes upon him and knew that she compared him to the young and wild Lisha she had married. Then he reached for her hand and smiled at her.

Lisha had come to the seventy-fifth year of his life when one day Nelson Story came to visit him. The heroic old man was ninety years old. His life also had been filled with adventure. The fame of his cattle drives and his fearless encounters with wild Indians and wild road agents made the stuff of thrilling stories for the youngsters who sat listening at Grandpa Rouse's home that day.

"Not many of us old-timers are left, Lisha," Nelson Story said as he left the house. "Soon we'll be sleeping out there on the hill with Elliot and John Bozeman and the others."

Lisha replied, "You know, Nelson, I believe the best is yet to be."

About a month after Nelson's last visit, Lisha and Chat arose early one morning. With Lee and Claude, they paused to read Psalm 91 and have prayer. Lee and Claude then hurried away to a neighbor's ranch to fire up the old steam engine and oil the machinery for the day's threshing. After breakfast, Lisha put on his hat and left the house on foot for town.

Returning from Bozeman, Lisha passed by the neighbor's place where Lee and Claude were harvesting at the time. The men were washing up for supper after a hard day's work when he arrived. Although urged to stay and eat with the crew, he declined, explaining that he had been gone all day and Chat would worry about him.

One wonders what his thoughts might have been as he approached the railroad crossing that evening. Gratitude for the golden grain that poured into the wagon box at harvesttime? Reminiscences of his encounter with Indians only forty or fifty rods from that crossing? The old lawless days when men like Plummer and Stinson fell into the hands of the vigilantes?

Engrossed in his thoughts, and quite deaf, he watched a freight train pass—then he stepped in front of an engine on the other track.

The years have come and gone since that tragedy. Those who pioneered the West have long since passed away. Elisha's children have scattered. His grandchildren and great-grandchildren have lived in many parts of the world, some serving as missionaries, doctors, nurses, teachers, and ministers. But the objective for which he labored—a settlement in the wilderness of western Montana where peace, order, and prosperity reign—has been fully realized.

# GOD'S VIEW OF HELLFIRE

### Q Why did God give His only begotten Son to the world?

"For God so loved the world, that he gave his only begotten Son, that whosoever believeth in him should not perish, but have everlasting life" (John 3:16).

### Q What will happen to those who do not repent?

"I tell you, Nay: but, except ye repent, ye shall all likewise perish" (Luke 13:3).

### Q To what are the wicked in their punishment compared?

"But the wicked shall perish, and the enemies of the Lord shall be as the fat of lambs: they shall consume; into smoke shall they consume away" (Psalm 37:20).

### Q What will be the character of this death?

"The Lord Jesus shall be revealed from heaven with his mighty angels, in flaming fire taking vengeance on them that know not God, and that obey not the gospel of our Lord Jesus Christ: who shall be punished with everlasting destruction from the presence of the Lord, and from the glory of his power" (2 Thessalonians 1:7–9).

### Q How does John the Baptist describe this destruction?

"Whose fan [winnowing fork] is in his hand, and he will throughly purge his floor, and gather his wheat into the garner; but he will burn up the chaff with unquenchable fire" (Matthew 3:12).

Not just burn them, but burn them up. The Bible says the wicked will die, be destroyed, perish. All of these words indicate total and complete annihilation of existence.

Unquenchable fire is fire that cannot be put out. Of course, it goes out by itself when its fuel is exhausted (compare Jeremiah 7:20 with 2 Chronicles 36:19 and Nehemiah 2:3).

### Q For whom was this fire originally prepared?

"Then shall he say also unto them on the left hand, Depart from me, ye cursed, into everlasting fire, prepared for the devil and his angels" (Matthew 25:41).

This fire is called eternal or "everlasting" (Greek *aionion,* meaning "age lasting"), not because it lasts forever, but because its results last forever.

## Q What Old Testament cities were burned with eternal fire?

"Even as Sodom and Gomorrha, and the cities about them in like manner, giving themselves over to fornication, and going after strange flesh, are set forth for an example, suffering the vengeance of eternal fire" (Jude 7).

"And turning the cities of Sodom and Gomorrha into ashes condemned them with an overthrow, making them an ensample unto those that after should live ungodly" (2 Peter 2:6).

Sodom and Gomorrah are given as examples of what will happen to the wicked. These cities were reduced to ashes, yet the text says they were burned with "eternal fire." However, Sodom is not still burning now. It was the result—not the process—that made the fire eternal. The "eternal fire" of hell will likewise go out, but its results (annihilation) will last forever.

Notice these expressions where "eternal" and "everlasting" refer to the result, not the process: "eternal salvation" (Hebrews 5:9); "eternal judgment" (Hebrews 6:2); "eternal damnation" (Mark 3:29); "everlasting punishment" (Matthew 25:46); "everlasting destruction" (2 Thessalonians 1:9). It is not *the process* (the saving, the judging, the sinning, the punishing, and the destroying) that is eternal—it is *the result* (salvation, judgment, sin, punishment, destruction). When Scripture speaks of "everlasting *punishment*" or "everlasting destruction," it does not mean eternal *punishing* or destroying. The penalty is eternal death (*punishment*), not eternal torment (*punishing*).

Like Sodom, the wicked will be burned with eternal fire, which will reduce them to ashes and then go out. That is what "everlasting destruction" means.

Matthew 25:46 says that the wicked "shall go away into everlasting punishment: but the righteous into life eternal." Those who believe in an eternally burning hell suggest that the "everlasting punishment" here must last just as long as the "life eternal" mentioned alongside it. They are quite correct: the penalty of eternal death does last just as long as the reward of eternal life. Remember: *punishment,* not *punishing;* eternal extinction, not eternal torture. Result, not process.

## Q Will any part of the wicked be left?

"For, behold, the day cometh, that shall burn as an oven; and all the proud, yea, and all that do wickedly, shall be stubble: and the day that cometh shall burn them up, saith the LORD of hosts, that it shall leave them neither root nor branch" (Malachi 4:1).

## Q How completely will the wicked be destroyed in hell?

"And fear not them which kill the body, but are not able to kill the soul: but rather fear him which is able to destroy both soul and body in hell" (Matthew 10:28).

Hell destroys the entire person, leaving nothing behind to suffer. Scripture never says that the soul is immortal and indestructible, but says that "the soul that sinneth, it shall die" (Ezekiel 18:4).

## Q When are the wicked dead raised for final punishment?

"The rest of the dead lived not again until the thousand years were finished" (Revelation 20:5).

## Q What is the origin of this fire?

"They [the unrighteous] went up on the breadth of the earth, and compassed the camp of the saints about, and the beloved city: and fire came down from God out of heaven, and devoured them" (Revelation 20:9).

In Isaiah 28:21, this work of destruction is called God's "strange act" and His "strange work" because it seems so contrary to His character of love. But by this means God will once and forever cleanse the universe of sin and all its sad results.

## Q What will be left of the wicked?

"And ye shall tread down the wicked; for they shall be ashes under the soles of your feet in the day that I shall do this, saith the LORD of hosts" (Malachi 4:3).

The wicked are to be utterly destroyed—consumed away into smoke, brought to ashes. Through sin they have forfeited the right to life and an immortal existence. Their destruction will, in fact, be an act of love and mercy on the part of God; to perpetuate their lives would only be to perpetuate sin and suffering.

## Q What will happen afterward?

"And I saw a new heaven and a new earth: for the first heaven and the first earth were passed away; and there was no more sea" (Revelation 21:1).

"Nevertheless we, according to his promise, look for new heavens and a new earth, wherein dwelleth righteousness" (2 Peter 3:13).

In due time, Jesus will cleanse this world from sin and sinners, restore it to Edenic perfection, and give it to the saints for an everlasting possession (Daniel 7:18, 22, 27).

## Q What is the essence and nature of God?

"God is love" (1 John 4:16).

There are overwhelming logical and philosophical difficulties with the concept of a God who subjects His finite creatures to infinite torture for their faults. We would not think very highly of a king who tortured his lame subjects because they could not keep up in royal races, and it would not help matters at all if the king made exceptions only for friends of his son! In comparison with a God of endless torment, Adolf Hitler was a paragon of tender mercy.

It seems clear that Scripture does not teach that the lost will be tortured forever by a God whose unfathomable love is matched only by His insatiable cruelty.

## Q After the Crucifixion, what day was kept by the women who followed Jesus?

"And they returned, and prepared spices and ointments; and rested the sabbath day according to the commandment" (Luke 23:56).

## Q In what instruction to His disciples did Christ show that He expected them to keep the Sabbath after His ascension?

"But pray ye that your flight be not in the winter, neither on the sabbath day" (Matthew 24:20).

The flight of the Christians took place late in October A.D. 66, three-and-one-half years before the fall of Jerusalem. Jesus clearly expected His followers to reverence and value the Sabbath *after* His ascension to heaven.

## Q On what day did Jesus worship?

"And he came to Nazareth, where he had been brought up: and, as his custom was, he went into the synagogue on the sabbath day, and stood up for to read" (Luke 4:16).

## Q On what day did Paul preach to the women at Philippi?

"And on the sabbath we went out of the city by a river side, where prayer was wont to be made; and we sat down, and spake unto the women which resorted thither" (Acts 16:13).

These verses confirm the early Christian church continued to call the seventh day the Sabbath, just as the Jews did.

## Q What did Jesus say about the Law and those who set it aside?

"Think not that I am come to destroy the law, or the prophets: I am not come to destroy, but to fulfil. For verily I say unto you, till heaven and earth pass, one jot or one tittle shall in no wise pass from the law, till all be fulfilled. Whosoever therefore shall break one of these least commandments, and shall teach men so, he shall be called the least in the kingdom of heaven: but whosoever shall do and teach them, the same shall be called great in the kingdom of heaven" (Matthew 5:17–19).

It is evident that all Ten Commandments are binding on Christians and that Christ had no thought of changing any of them—including the Sabbath of the fourth commandment. But most Christians keep the first day of the week instead. Many believe that Christ changed the Sabbath. But, from His own words, we see that He came for no such purpose. Jesus never taught nor expected the Sabbath to be changed.

## Q How did this change in observance of days come about?

Through a *gradual* transference.

"The Christian Church made no formal, but a gradual and almost unconscious, transference of the one day to the other" (F. W. Farrar, *The Voice From Sinai,* p. 167).

## Q For how long a time was the seventh-day Sabbath observed in the Christian church?

The church historian Socrates, who wrote in the fifth century, says, "Almost all the churches throughout the world celebrate the sacred mysteries on the Sabbath of every week, yet the Christians of Alexandria and at Rome, on account of some ancient tradition, have ceased to do this" (*Ecclesiastical History*, bk. 5, chap. 22, in *A Select Library of Nicene and Post-Nicene Fathers*, 2nd Series, vol. 2, p. 32).

## Q Who first enforced Sunday keeping by law?

The Roman emperor Constantine the Great.

"On the venerable day of the sun let the magistrates and people residing in cities rest, and let all workshops be closed. In the country, however, persons engaged in agriculture may freely and lawfully continue their pursuits; because it often happens that another day is not so suitable for grain sowing or for vine planting; lest by neglecting the proper moment for such operations the bounty of heaven should be lost. (Given the 7th day of March, Crispus and Constantine being consuls each of them for the second time.)" (*Codex Justinianus*, bk. 3, title 12, sec. 3; translated in Philip Schaff, *History of the Christian Church* [Scribner's, 1902 ed.], vol. 3, p. 380).

This edict, issued by Constantine, first opened the way for the union of church and state in the Roman Empire. It was an important step in bringing about and establishing the change of the Sabbath.

## Q What testimony does Eusebius bear on this subject?

"All things whatsoever that it was duty to do on the Sabbath, these we [the church] have transferred to the Lord's day" (translated from Eusebius, *Commentary on the Psalms*, in Migne, *Patrologia Graeca*, vol. 23, cols. 1171, 1172).

The change of the Sabbath was the result of the combined efforts of church and state, and it took centuries to accomplish it. Eusebius of Caesarea (270–338) was a noted bishop of the church, biographer and flatterer of Constantine, and the reputed father of ecclesiastical history.

## Q By what church council was the observance of the seventh day forbidden, and Sunday observance enjoined?

The Council of Laodicea, in Asia Minor, in the fourth century.

Canon 29 reads, "Christians shall not Judaize and be idle on Saturday [*sabbato*, the Sabbath], but shall work on that day; but the Lord's day they shall especially honor, and, as being Christians, shall, if possible, do no work on that day. If, however, they are found Judaizing, they shall be shut out [*anathema*] from Christ" (Charles Joseph Hefele, *A History of the Councils of the Church* [1896 English ed.], vol. 2, p. 316).

## Q What influence do the Bible and history speak of working in the church immediately after the apostolic days?

"Also of your own selves shall men arise, speaking perverse things, to draw away disciples after them" (Acts 20:30).

"Between the days of the apostles and the conversion of Constantine, the Christian commonwealth changed its aspect. . . . Rites and ceremonies, of which neither Paul nor Peter ever heard, crept silently into use, and then claimed the rank of divine institutions" (W. D. Killen, *The Ancient Church*, pp. xv, xvi).

## Q What did Christ say of worship based on tradition?

"But in vain they do worship me, teaching for doctrines the commandments of men" (Matthew 15:9).

Jesus never quibbled with the Pharisees about the proper day of worship. They all agreed that the seventh day was Sabbath. What He took issue with is the way they worshiped. He was saddened by all the man-made rules that burdened the sacred day of rest.

## Q Whose commands should we obey in all religious matters?

"We ought to obey God rather than men" (Acts 5:29).

In all matters of faith and practice Christians should carefully consider the life and teachings of Jesus Christ. To His disciples, He said, "Go ye therefore, and teach all nations, . . . teaching them to observe all things whatsoever I have commanded you" (Matthew 28:19, 20).

*FREE Lessons at www.BibleStudies.com*

**Call:**
1-888-456-7933

**Write:**
Discover
P.O. Box 53055
Los Angeles, CA 90053

## It's easy to learn more about the Bible!